To request permissions, contact the publisher at bczpublishers@gmail.com.

Paperback: ISBN 978-1-7367153-5-2

Second Paperback Edition: October 2021

Illustrated by: Cynthia Zeilenga

BCZ Publishers
3365 E. Miraloma Ave. #205, Anaheim, CA 92806

Becoming What You Receive

Dear Lord, please guide

_____
(your name here)

throughout this First Communion Journey.

I am so humbled that you have chosen this activity book to guide your children through this very special Sacrament. This book was lovingly written in order to lay a foundation, not just for their First Communion, but for a lifetime relationship with our Lord and Savior.

Growing up Maronite Catholic, a great love for Jesus was instilled in my heart through the efforts of my parents, my Christian schooling, and our Church. However, it was not until hardship struck my family that I began to dig deeper and truly search for refuge in the heart of our faith. By the Grace of God, I was able to not only strengthen my faith, but also learn so much that I wish I had known earlier in my life.

Through our years of teaching Sunday school, my mother, Christiane, and I began to put together a curriculum with that notion in mind. With this book, our hope is to introduce children to these concepts at an early age and ignite a love and curiosity for our Lord that will extend well beyond their First Communion.

This is a very Bible centered activity book and it is recommended that you purchase a full length children's Catholic Bible in order for the children to understand the concepts. Each chapter starts with a "Memory Verse" intended to introduce the topic and help children understand that all the elements of our faith stem from the Bible. Bible verses are referenced throughout the chapters of the book to get children comfortable with navigating through the Word of the Lord with ease.

Children learn best when they are interactive and having fun. That is why each chapter has an activity for them to be creative and hands on. Your involvement and enthusiasm throughout this journey will be invaluable to their growth. Children have the incredible ability to make us view concepts we have lived with our entire lives with fresh eyes. Therefore, it is my prayer, that children, parents, and teachers alike, will all grow in their faith after this First Communion Journey has come to an end.

You and your families are in our prayers, always!

With God's Blessings,

Cynthia ♥

a very special thank you to all the clergy and teachers that made this little idea, a reality. especially Joseph Waked and Sister Martha Mechleb.

this book is dedicated to my family,

my bestest friend,

and my bez.

1 Peter 4:8

Table of Contents

CHAPTER 1

God's Love Through the Bible

MEMORY VERSE: John 3:16

"For God loved the world so much that He gave His only Son, so that everyone who believes in Him may not die but have eternal life."

WHO IS GOD?

God is the Creator of everything. He created heaven, earth, and all things. He is perfect, all powerful, and knows everything.

In God there are three different, but equal Divine Persons – God the Father, God the Son (Jesus), and God the Holy Spirit. This is called the Trinity and we will learn more about that in chapter 4.

He created us in His image to know Him, love Him, and to serve Him in this world and to be happy with Him forever in heaven. All because of His great love for us.

GOD IS LOVE

Love is at the core of our lives. Because we are followers of Jesus, we should love everyone around us the way He did.

Look closely at the picture of Jesus on the cross. He loves us so very much.

He did not have to come down to earth. He was in heaven with His Father. But He chose to come and go through humiliation, suffering, and even death just to save us.

We are sinners and needed to be saved. When we do things that are wrong we can hurt God, other people, and even ourselves. These wrong things are called sins. When we commit these sins, we are telling God that we do not want to be His friends anymore. So because we are sinners, we needed a way to become clean and return to friendship with God so that we can get to heaven and be with Him.

In this chapter's Memory Verse, we can see that God the Father and His only Son, Jesus, love us so much that they had a plan to save us. Throughout the Bible we get to learn about God and His great love for us.

WHAT IS THE BIBLE?

The words of the Bible were given by God to human writers who were holy. Because the words come from God, they are like love letters that God the Father wrote to us, His children. They are so precious to us and we need to cherish them.

The Bible is a collection of 73 books split into two sections – The Old Testament (the stories of God's people before Jesus came to earth) and The New Testament (the stories of Jesus and His disciples). The New Testament is split into two groups – The Gospels (the stories of Jesus' life and His works) and The Letters (written by His disciples to teach about God and how we should live). On the next page you can see all of the books of the Bible in order.

THE 73 BOOKS OF THE BIBLE

Even though Bibles have page numbers, we do not use them to navigate through. There are 73 Books in the Bible (listed in order on the bookshelf) and finding a particular verse is as easy as shown below!

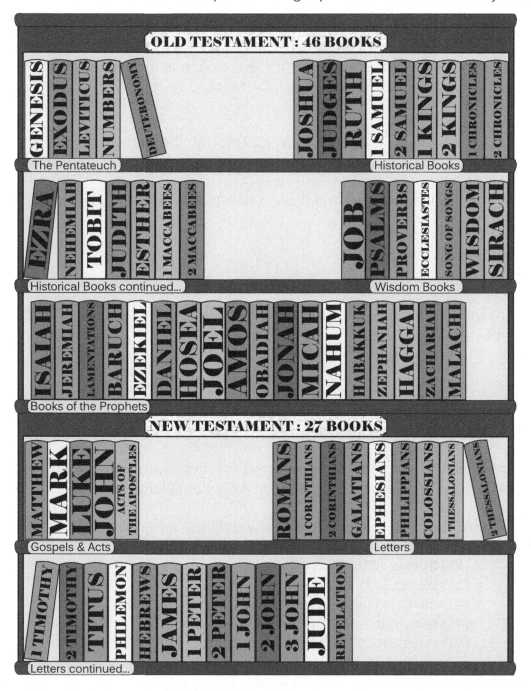

OLD TESTAMENT : 46 BOOKS

GENESIS · EXODUS · LEVITICUS · NUMBERS · DEUTERONOMY
The Pentateuch

JOSHUA · JUDGES · RUTH · 1 SAMUEL · 2 SAMUEL · 1 KINGS · 2 KINGS · 1 CHRONICLES · 2 CHRONICLES
Historical Books

EZRA · NEHEMIAH · TOBIT · JUDITH · ESTHER · 1 MACCABEES · 2 MACCABEES
Historical Books continued...

JOB · PSALMS · PROVERBS · ECCLESIASTES · SONG OF SONGS · WISDOM · SIRACH
Wisdom Books

ISAIAH · JEREMIAH · LAMENTATIONS · BARUCH · EZEKIEL · DANIEL · HOSEA · JOEL · AMOS · OBADIAH · JONAH · MICAH · NAHUM · HABAKKUK · ZEPHANIAH · HAGGAI · ZACHARIAH · MALACHI
Books of the Prophets

NEW TESTAMENT : 27 BOOKS

MATTHEW · MARK · LUKE · JOHN · ACTS OF THE APOSTLES
Gospels & Acts

ROMANS · 1 CORINTHIANS · 2 CORINTHIANS · GALATIANS · EPHESIANS · PHILIPPIANS · COLOSSIANS · 1 THESSALONIANS · 2 THESSALONIANS
Letters

1 TIMOTHY · 2 TIMOTHY · TITUS · PHILEMON · HEBREWS · JAMES · 1 PETER · 2 PETER · 1 JOHN · 2 JOHN · 3 JOHN · JUDE · REVELATION
Letters continued...

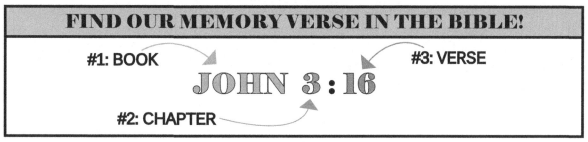

FIND OUR MEMORY VERSE IN THE BIBLE!

#1: BOOK   #3: VERSE

JOHN 3 : 16

#2: CHAPTER

☆**FIRST:** Find the Bible book.
☆**SECOND:** Turn to the chapter in that book (the large number).
☆**THIRD:** Find the verse number within the chapter (the small number next to the text).

THE BIBLE & ITS CONTENT

Open your Bible to Hebrews 4:12a:

In this verse, St. Paul is explaining that the words of the Bible are ALIVE.
The Word of God is alive and when we read it, it becomes alive in us.

If prayer is a way that we can talk to God, then reading the Bible is a way that God can talk to us. Because His Word is alive, He speaks to us and teaches us through it. You might hear someone say that the Bible is old or out of date. But, because it is alive, 2,000 years after it was written, the words in it still apply to us in our daily lives today.

WHAT ARE PARABLES?

Parables are stories that Jesus told His followers. Through the parables in the Gospels, Jesus teaches us how we should act, treat other people, and, above all, how to fully love God.

There are so many important stories that Jesus preached that teach us valuable lessons for our lives.

THE PRODIGAL SON

Open your Bible to Luke 15:11-32:

☆ What does this story mean to you?
☆ Who does the father represent in this parable?
☆ Who do the sons represent?

now.... ACT IT OUT !

To better understand the parable, act it out with two people:

Person #1 never follows the rules. Person #1 is considered to be a bad person.
Person #2 always follows the rules. Person #2 is considered to be a good person.

What are good and bad things that these two different people might do? Here are some examples for you to act out:

☆ (#1) throws fits, (#2) is nice
☆ (#1) steals, (#2) shares
☆ (#1) calls people bad names, (#2) says nice things
☆ (#1) is lazy at school, (#2) works very hard
☆ (#1) never goes to Church, (#2) goes to Church every Sunday

Who appears to be doing all the right things, (#1) or (#2)?
Who does God love more? (#1) or (#2)?

Jesus is showing us that God loves <u>EVERYONE</u>. But many times people who appear to be doing the right things in life, think that they are better than the people who might not be. This is a parable that Jesus told to show that both kinds of people need forgiveness and that God wants to save everyone.

The father in this parable shows us what God is like. The brothers show us what we are like. The point is that God wants to save both the people who follow the rules and people who break the rules. All we have to do is turn to Him and He will come running to us. He loves us so much and there is room for everyone in the Kingdom of Heaven!

Name: _____

THE PRODIGAL SON

Jesus tells the story of two very different sons and one very loving and forgiving father. Here we learn about how we should be merciful with each other, just as our Heavenly Father is merciful with us. (Luke 15:11-32)

Read each verse, and number the events of the story in the right order.

1   Luke 15:12-13

2   Luke 15:14

3   Luke 15:17-19

4   Luke 15:20

5   Luke 15:28-30

6   Luke 15:31-32

_____ The father runs to welcome his younger son, hugs and kisses him

_____ The younger son comes to realize that he has sinned and decides to return to his father's house

_____ The older son gets upset that his younger brother is welcomed back with a feast and celebration

_____ The younger son starves and is left with nothing

_____ The father explains that both sons are loved so much and are always welcome in his home

_____ The younger son took his share of the property and money and left his father's home

MEANING OF THE PARABLE:

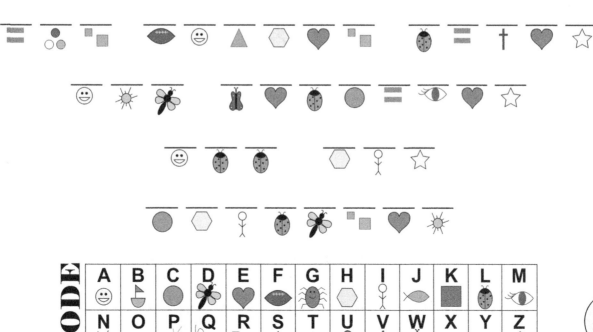

THE THREE SERVANTS

Jesus tells a story of three servants who used what their master had given them differently. In this parable, we learn that we have each been given gifts from God that we should use and not waste. (Matthew 25:14-30)

Read each verse, and number the events of the story in the right order.

1   Matthew 25:14-15

2   Matthew 25:16

3   Matthew 25:17

4   Matthew 25:18

5   Matthew 25:19-23

6   Matthew 25:26-30

____ The servant who had 1,000 coins dug a hole in the ground and hid the money

____ The master punishes the servant who buried the money and throws him into the darkness

____ The master leaves his servants in charge of his property, splitting it according to their abilities

____ The servant who had 5,000 coins invested and doubled the money

____ The servants who doubled their money and used it wisely were greatly rewarded when their master returned

____ The servant who had 2,000 coins invested and doubled the money

MEANING OF THE PARABLE:

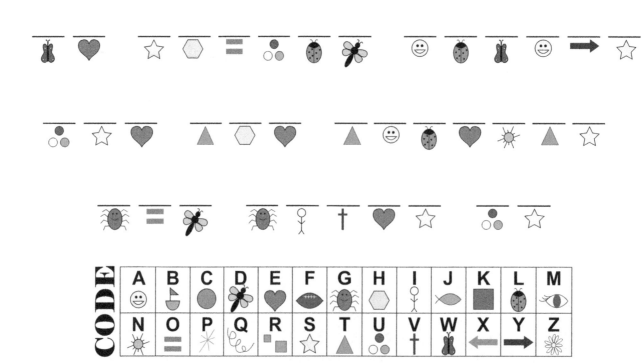

12

CHAPTER 2
Guardian Angels, Saints, & 3T's

MEMORY VERSE: Psalm 91:11

"God will put His angels in charge of you to protect you wherever you go."

GUARDIAN ANGELS

Because there is sin and evil all around us, from the moment we are born, God assigns a Guardian Angel to protect and help each one of us in our lives.

We can find Guardian Angels in this chapter's Memory Verse. God loves us so much that He wants to make sure we are always protected and taken care of.

SAINTS

We not only have Guardian Angels that can help us, but God has also given us saints. A saint is someone who lived a life so holy and pleasing to God that they are now in heaven with Him. These people were just like us – they shared in the same struggles, sins, and hardships that we do. They have been in similar situations and despite everything, they persevered with Jesus by their side. Since the beginning of Christianity, the Catholic Church has canonized (or officially declared to be a saint) over 10,000 people. Saints can be any age, gender, or race - it is all about the life that they lived and how they used their time on earth to serve Jesus and others.

God has given us saints to pray for us. Just like we pray for one another, when you ask a saint to pray for you, you are asking someone who is closest to God to pray for you. How powerful is that! Anyone can be a saint, it is our ultimate goal and what we should always work towards. We just need to love God and serve Him with our whole hearts. Try to think of some examples of saints... there are so many!

THE 3 T's – TIME, TALENT, & TREASURE

T#1 - TIME

Our time on earth starts when we are born and ends with our death. We do not know how much time we will have, but we know that it is very precious. God wants all of us to reach heaven. That is why He created us and why He sent Jesus to be our Savior.

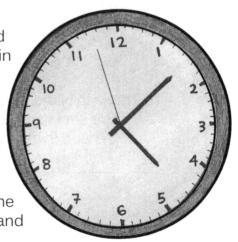

Our life is one big journey to heaven – each day, week, month, and year should be getting us closer to heaven. We cannot get closer in our journey unless we give some time to God.

What are some examples of giving our time to God?
- ☆ **PRAYER:** This is the best way to develop a personal relationship with God – praising Him, thanking Him, sharing with Him our successes and failures, and asking for His guidance in our daily lives.
- ☆ **READING THE BIBLE:** Prayer is us talking to God. Reading the Bible is God talking to us. It helps us reflect on God's Word and reminds us of His great love for us.
- ☆ **HELPING OTHERS:** This is another way to share our personal time. We show our love for Him by letting Christ use our hands, our feet, our eyes, and our voice for the glory of God.

Open your Bible to Matthew 25:31-46:

Jesus explains that whenever you help anyone in need it is like you are helping Him. Therefore, when you use your time to do something for others, you are on the right path on your journey to heaven.

T#2 - TALENT

All of us have special talents and gifts that God has given us. These talents and gifts are not given to us just for our own use, but to make other people's lives around us better too – which is another way we serve God.

For example, if you have a beautiful singing voice, that is a wonderful gift from God. You can use that gift to make other people's lives better and serve God by sharing your voice and singing in Church.

Open your Bible to 1 Peter 4:10:

St. Peter explains that we each have special gifts and we MUST use them for the good of others around us.

Another talent we all have is making people happy and feel good. We can use our time and talent to do any of the below examples:

- ☆ Visit the sick and elderly
- ☆ Teach those who want to learn
- ☆ Pray for each other
- ☆ Feed the hungry
- ☆ Console the lonely
- ☆ Be kind

Christ depends on each one of us to do these works in His name. That makes us coworkers with Jesus in his Holy Works. What a blessing!

T#3 - TREASURE

We all have been blessed with so much. It is our duty to give back to God and the Church and to those who do not have as much as we do.

Open your Bible to Matthew 6:21:

When we are able to give of our money instead of keeping it for ourselves, it shows that our heart is not tied to our money and that we love God more than any material things in this world.

☆ To God and the Church:

Because God is the Giver, some percentage of what is received must be returned to Him as an act of gratitude.

☆ To Those in Need:

We should share some of our money and material goods with those in need in our family, community, and around the world.

─────────────── ☆ ACTIVITY ☆ ───────────────

Get a jar and set it aside for your "Treasure." Throughout your First Communion Journey, put a part of your allowance, money you may get on your birthday or Christmas, or just change you find, in this jar. At the end of the year, gather all the money in the jar and give half of it to the Church, and give the other half to someone in need.

Name: _____

The 3 T's

1. What are the 3 T's?

_____ _____ _____

2. How can you give your TIME to God?

_____

_____

_____

3. How can you give your TALENTS to God?

_____

_____

_____

4. How can you give your TREASURE to God?

_____

_____

_____

My Guardian Angel & Me

Draw a picture of your Guardian Angel and you together.

Prayer to My Guardian Angel

Angel of God, my guardian dear,
to whom God's love commits me here,
ever this day be at my side,
to light and guard, to rule and guide.
Amen.

Choose a saint to pray for you throughout your First Communion Journey!

ALL ABOUT

Paste or draw a picture of this saint:

I am the Patron of:

_____

_____

_____

_____

_____

My Feast Day is:

_____

I am from: _____

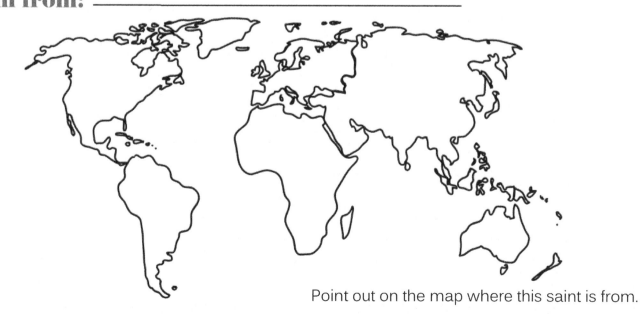

Point out on the map where this saint is from.

My Saint Project

1. When and where was your saint born?

_____

_____

2. Give a brief description of your saint's parents, family, and early life.

_____

_____

_____

_____

_____

3. Was your saint a martyr?

_____

4. How and when did your saint pass away?

_____

_____

_____

5. What was your saint's job in this world (priest, nun, bishop, carpenter, artist, teacher, doctor, etc.)?

_____

_____

6. What miracles has your saint performed?

_____

_____

_____

7. When was your saint canonized (become a saint)?

_____

8. What three events in the life of your saint stand out the most to you? Why?

_____

_____

_____

_____

9. Name one way your saint showed love for others.

_____

_____

_____

10. In what two ways was your saint most like Jesus?

_____

_____

_____

11. How can you be more like this saint in your daily life today? Be specific.

_____

_____

_____

_____

_____

_____

12. How do you think this saint will inspire you in your life?

_____

_____

_____

_____

_____

CHAPTER 3

Core Prayers

MEMORY VERSE: 1 Thessalonians 5:16-18

"Be joyful always, pray at all times, be thankful in all circumstances. This is what God wants from you in your life in union with Christ Jesus."

In this chapter, we will learn the core prayers of our faith: the Lord's Prayer, Hail Mary, Doxology, Nicene Creed, along with the meaning of each. These prayers are so important and will help us in "praying at all times" as St. Paul says in the above Memory Verse.

THE LORD'S PRAYER

Jesus Himself gave us the Lord's Prayer and taught us how to pray it. This prayer reminds us to do the right thing so that we can keep our friendship with God.

Open your Bible to Matthew 6:9-13 to find this prayer.

Let us break the prayer down line by line to understand the meaning.

Our Father, who art in heaven, hallowed be thy name
He is OUR HEAVENLY FATHER. We call on Him like we call on our own parents – but even more so. Hallowed means holy and this is how we praise God.

Thy kingdom come; thy will be done on earth as it is in heaven
We are promising to honor and obey God.

Give us this day, our daily bread
We ask God to give us what we need today. Nothing more, nothing less.

And forgive us our trespasses as we forgive those who trespass against us
Trespasses means sins or the things that we do wrong. We are saying that we are sorry for our sins and are also promising to forgive others. We cannot be forgiven our own sins if we do not forgive others their sins.

And lead us not into temptation but deliver us from evil
We ask God to help us be good and protect us from evil.

Amen
We agree!

THE HAIL MARY

2000 years ago, God the Son became a man – Jesus Christ. This happened because He was born from a human mother, the Virgin Mary. Everything that made Him human, He got from His mother. Jesus loved and honored His mother perfectly and He made her holy. In a similar way, He wants us to honor her the way He did. The Hail Mary is a prayer we pray to honor the Mother of Jesus. We love her and honor her because she is our Mother and the best example of the most holy human.

Open your Bible to Luke 1:28 and then to Luke 1:41-43 to find where this prayer comes from.

Let us break the prayer down line by line to understand the meaning.

Hail Mary, full of Grace, the Lord is with thee (you)
This comes from Gabriel's greeting to Mary when he was announcing that she will become pregnant with the baby Jesus. The Church later added her name. Mary is "full of grace" because she was born without sin, remained faithful to the Lord, and never sinned her whole life. In order for her to be the Mother of God, she had to be pure. She is full of grace because the Lord is with her, and the Lord is with her because she is full of grace.

Blessed are thou among women and blessed is the fruit of thy womb, Jesus.
Mary was pregnant with Jesus when she found out her much older cousin, Elizabeth, was also pregnant (with John the Baptist). Mary traveled very far to help take care of her. In greeting her cousin, Elizabeth said to Mary "blessed are thou among women." Mary is blessed because she believed in God's plan of salvation and she said "yes" to this very big task that God had given her. She is blessed and the fruit of her womb (what came from her womb) is THE most blessed.

Holy Mary, mother of God,
Elizabeth also says this to Mary in Luke 1:43 – "Why should this great thing happen to me, that my Lord's mother comes to visit me" Because through her "yes" and obedience, we have Jesus who is God – making Mary the mother of God.

Pray for us sinners, now and at the hour of our death
We ask Mary to pray for us because we are sinners and ask her to accompany us through our lives. We trust that she will always pray for us, now and always.

Amen
We agree!

THE DOXOLOGY

The Doxology is one of two beautiful little prayers to the Holy Trinity (the other is the Sign of the Cross).

The Holy Trinity is our one God in three Persons – God the Father, God the Son, and God the Holy Spirit.

Here is the prayer in full:

Glory be to the Father, and to the Son, and to the Holy Spirit.
As it was in the beginning is now and ever shall be, world without end, Amen.

THE NICENE CREED

The Nicene Creed is a declaration of our Catholic faith. Let us break the prayer down line by line to understand the meaning:

We believe in one God, the Father, the Almighty, maker of heaven and earth, of all things visible and invisible.

This part of the Nicene Creed is about God, the Father. We are declaring that we believe in God the Father, who created us. Because of His great love for us, He created us to share eternity with Him.

We believe in one Lord, Jesus Christ, the only Son of God, born of the Father before all ages. God from God, Light from Light, true God from true God, begotten not made, consubstantial with the Father. Through Him all things were made. For us men and for our salvation He came down from heaven: and by the Holy Spirit was incarnate of the Virgin Mary, and became man. For our sake, He was crucified under Pontius Pilot; and rose again on the third day in accordance with the Scriptures; He ascended into heaven and is seated at the right hand of the Father. He will come again in glory to judge the living and the dead, and His kingdom will have no end.

This part of the Nicene Creed is about God, the Son. We are declaring that we believe in God, the Son, who suffered for us, died for us, and saved us – because He loves us. God, the Father, loves us so much that He sent His Son to pay for our sins so that we can be with Him in heaven. Through our friendship with Jesus and our obedience to Him and the Father, we can go to heaven to be with Him forever.

We believe in the Holy Spirit, the Lord, the giver of life, who proceeds from the Father and the Son. Who with the Father and the Son is adored and glorified. Who has spoken through the Prophets.

This part of the Nicene Creed is about God, the Holy Spirit. We are declaring that we believe in God, the Holy Spirit, who lives in us (through Baptism) and guides us. The Holy Spirit is the third Person of the Holy Trinity and is the love between the Father and the Son. The Holy Spirit helps us love God and guides us in life to be close to Jesus so we can go to heaven.

The first section of the Nicene Creed is us stating that we believe in the Holy Trinity – One God, three Persons.

The last section of the Nicene Creed is us confirming what we believe and our response to God's great love for us.

**We believe in one Holy Catholic and apostolic Church. We confess one baptism for the forgiveness of sins. And we look forward to the resurrection of the dead, and life of the world to come.
AMEN.**

The Lord's Prayer

Our Father, Who art in heaven,
Hallowed be Thy Name.
Thy Kingdom come.
Thy Will be done, on earth as it is in Heaven.
Give us this day our daily bread.
And forgive us our trespasses,
as we forgive those who trespass against us.
And lead us not into temptation,
but deliver us from evil

> For the kingdom, the power, and the glory
> are Yours now and forever

only recited during
Holy Mass celebrations

Amen.

The Hail Mary

Hail Mary full of Grace, the Lord is with thee.
Blessed are thou among women
and blessed is the fruit of thy womb Jesus.
Holy Mary Mother of God,
pray for us sinners now and at the hour of our death
Amen.

The Doxology

Glory be to the Father, and to the Son,
and to the Holy Spirit, as it was in the beginning,
is now, and ever shall be, world without end.
Amen.

Nicene Creed

We believe in one God, the Father, the Almighty,
maker of heaven and earth, of all things visible and invisible.
We believe in one Lord, Jesus Christ, the only Son of God,
born of the Father before all ages,
God from God, Light from Light,
true God from true God,
begotten, not made, consubstantial with the Father.
Through Him all things were made.
For us men and for our salvation He came down from heaven;
and by the Holy Spirit
was incarnate of the Virgin Mary, and became man.
For our sake He was crucified under Pontius Pilate,
He suffered death and was buried, and rose again on the third day
in accordance with the Scriptures;
He ascended into heaven and is seated at the right hand of the Father.
He will come again in glory to judge the living and the dead,
and His kingdom will have no end.
We believe in the Holy Spirit, the Lord, the giver of life,
who proceeds from the Father and the Son.
Who with the Father and the Son is adored and glorified.
Who has spoken through the Prophets.
We believe in one, holy, Catholic, and Apostolic Church.
We confess one baptism for the forgiveness of sins.
And we look forward to the resurrection of the dead,
and the life of the world to come.
Amen.

CHAPTER 4

The Trinity

MEMORY VERSE: 2 Corinthians 13:13

"The grace of the Lord Jesus Christ, the love of God, and the fellowship of the Holy Spirit be with you all."

THE STRUCTURE OF THE TRINITY

This chapter's Memory Verse is actually a verse that is said within different Holy Mass traditions. This verse brings together all three parts of the Trinity.

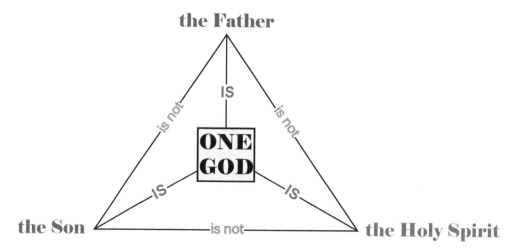

As shown in the above triangle, the name of God appears only one time. Why is that? Because there is only ONE God. This is extremely important! God cannot have an equal. It is impossible for there to be more than ONE God.

God has told us that in the ONE God, there are three Divine Persons. These three Persons are not three gods. Remember that is impossible to have more than ONE God. The three Persons are different Persons but they are still ONE God.

The Three Persons of the ONE God are:

The Father
The Son
The Holy Spirit

Notice in the Above Triangle:

The Father is NOT the Son and NOT the Holy Spirit
The Son is NOT the Father and NOT the Holy Spirit
The Holy Spirit is NOT the Father and NOT the Son

They are three Different Persons! But ...

The Father is God
The Son is God
The Holy Spirit is God

The three Persons make up only ONE God.

GOD THE FATHER

The entire Bible is about God, but we are going to pick out stories that show us more about each Person of God.

☆ What makes a good father?
> Loves you unconditionally, takes care of you, protects you, teaches you, etc...

Take whatever you think of as a good father and multiply that by a million – that is who God the Father is. Have you ever thought of God as your father? We say it every time we pray the Lord's Prayer when we say, "Our Father..."

Open your Bible to Matthew 6:25-34:
☆ What is Jesus telling us about God the Father?
> Look at how beautiful the flowers are. Look at the birds in the sky. They are so well taken care of and they have everything they need. If God the Father takes such good care of small things like flowers and birds, imagine how much He cares for and loves you. We should not worry about anything because God, our Father, is taking care of us, always.

Another wonderful reminder of God's love is our Memory Verse from chapter 1 – John 3:16.

GOD THE SON

☆ What makes a good friend?
> Loving, loyal, always there, will never leave you, will do anything for you, etc...

Have you ever thought of Jesus as your friend?

Open your Bible to John 15:7-17:
> Jesus is calling us His friends. He also goes further and says that there is no greater love than someone laying down His life for His friends.

What did Jesus do on Good Friday on the cross? He came JUST to lay down His life for us and save us. There is no greater love, no greater friend.

Also, Jesus is asking us to ask for things – ask and you shall receive. We might not always get the answer we want, but all of our prayers are always answered according to His will.

Remember, God always has our best interest in mind. For example, you can pray for 100 scoops of ice cream. God will answer that prayer, but most likely with a "no." Even though you want 100 scoops of ice cream, God knows that 100 scoops will hurt your stomach. We may not see it at the time, but He always guides us to what is best for us.

Also, what is Jesus emphasizing here? LOVE. If we do everything in love, our lives will be filled with joy and we will have peace through Jesus.

GOD THE HOLY SPIRIT

☆ What makes a good teacher?

Gives you knowledge, teaches you, is patient, is loving, gives you strength, etc...

Have you ever thought of the Holy Spirit as your teacher?

Open your Bible to Galatians 5:22-26:

St. Paul is explaining the difference between the nature of the Spirit and human nature. When we are guided by human nature, we fight, we are jealous, there is anger, etc.

However, when we follow the teachings of the Holy Spirit, we are given the gift of eternal life. When we live by the Spirit and others see our example, they will see the 9 fruits of the Spirit alive in us – love, joy, peace, patience, kindness, goodness, faithfulness, humility, and self-control.

If we allow the Holy Spirit to guide and teach us, we will be a shining example for others and continue in helping build the Kingdom of Heaven.

The Trinity

1. Who are the 3 Persons of the Trinity?

_____

_____

_____

2. Each Person of the Trinity helps us in different ways. Through the Bible, what role did we find for each Person?

God the Father - Matthew 6:25-34: _____

God the Son - John 15:7-17: _____

God the Holy Spirit - Galatians 5:22-26: _____

3. According to Galatians 5:22-23, what are the nine fruits of the Holy Spirit?

_____   _____

_____   _____

_____   _____

_____   _____

_____

Trinity Clover
⭐ ACTIVITY ⭐

WHAT YOU'LL NEED:
☆ Crayons
☆ Scissors
☆ 1 Paper Fastener Pin

INSTRUCTIONS:
1. Color each heart and cut them out.

2. Color the clover on the following page and cut it out.

3. Using a paper fastener pin, puncture the center of the clover and the bottom of each heart (about 1/2" up from bottom).

4. Stack each heart on paper fastener and place the fastener in the center of the clover.

5. Each heart should be fully mobile around and able to match accordingly.

HEARTS - cut out

GOD THE FATHER

GOD THE SON

GOD THE HOLY SPIRIT

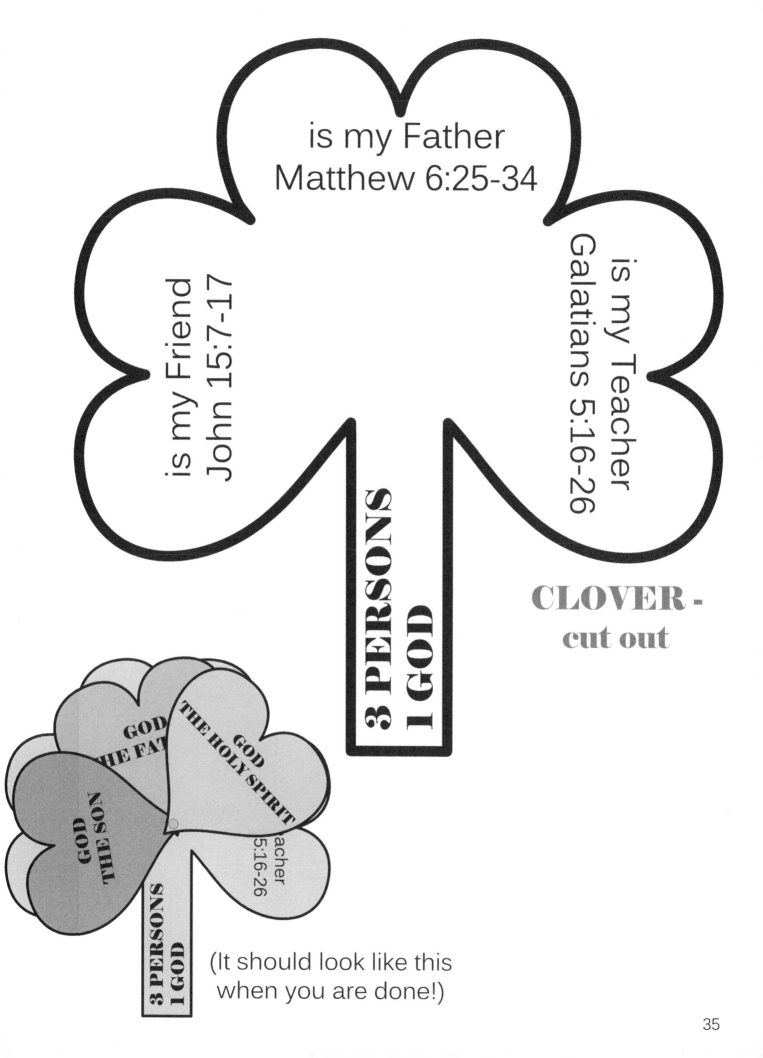

is my Father
Matthew 6:25-34

is my Friend
John 15:7-17

is my Teacher
Galatians 5:16-26

3 PERSONS
1 GOD

CLOVER -
cut out

GOD
THE FATHER

GOD
THE HOLY SPIRIT

GOD
THE SON

acher
5:16-26

3 PERSONS
1 GOD

(It should look like this
when you are done!)

CHAPTER 5

The Virgin Mary

"My heart praises the Lord; my soul is glad because of God my Savior, for He has remembered me, His lowly servant! From now on all people will call me happy, because of the great things the Mighty God has done for me. His name is holy."

INTRODUCTION TO THE VIRGIN MARY

When you were born, you became a member of a family. When you were baptized, you became a member of an even larger family – the Catholic Church. This Catholic Church family has a mother just like most families – The Virgin Mary.

When God sent the Angel Gabriel to tell Mary that she will be the mother of Jesus, her simple reply of "yes" made her not only the mother of Jesus, but the mother of God's family, the Church.

After Jesus ascended to heaven, Mary stayed on earth to take care of the Christian family and continue Jesus' ministry.

When Mary died, Jesus did something very special for His mother. When we die, our bodies will be buried in a grave and we will rise on the last day when Jesus comes back to earth. But because Mary was born without original sin and had been so special her whole life, she was taken up body and soul, into heaven. This is called the Assumption.

Mary takes care of us. She prays for us and asks Jesus to bless us. She helps us to be like Jesus so that we can live with Him forever.

MARY AS A PERSON

Sometimes we forget that Mary, Joseph, and Jesus were real people. They faced problems, hard times, and difficult choices. Just like us.

We do not know many details about her life, but we do know that she is the only human who lived perfectly and remained without sin. Jesus is perfect but He is not only fully human, but fully God as well (part of the Trinity). Mary is only fully human – making her the only perfect human.

Mary only shows up in the Gospel 7 times – the Annunciation, her Visitation to Elizabeth, the Nativity, the Presentation of Jesus, the Finding of Jesus in the Temple, the Wedding at Cana, and at the foot of the Cross.

Even though she only appears 7 times, each time is full of purpose and power and we can learn so much from her on how to be a good person, friend, daughter/son, and parent.

MARY'S SONG

Open your Bible to Luke 1:46-55: This is called "Mary's Song."

Mary's positivity and grateful attitude should be a shining example in our lives.

We all have been in upsetting or unfair situations. But whenever we start to feel overwhelmed or upset, we should remember Mary's example.

Instead of thinking about what has gone wrong or all that we do not have, we should remember all of God's blessings in our lives and how much love and good there is all around us. Keeping an attitude of gratitude will help make the light we have inside us shine even brighter.

When things are sad or upsetting, because we have the light of Jesus in our hearts, we should be like Mary so that no matter how hard things are, we are strong, positive, and grateful. We have God on our side, always. There is nothing to fear.

Our positivity and light should not be something we just talk about, it should be something we show by example – especially when life gets difficult.

now.... **ACT IT OUT!**

☆ Person #1 – does not have their lunch and is sitting by themselves
☆ Person #2 – points this out to all the others and makes fun of Person #1 – everyone starts laughing
☆ Person #3 – notices that Person #1 is alone and hungry and gets up to share their lunch and sit with them
☆ Person #4 – sees Person #3 and is inspired by their example. They sit together and all share their food

Always choose to let your light shine brightly and be kind. You never know who you can inspire along the way!

AT THE FOOT OF THE CROSS

Open your Bible to John 19:25-27.

Notice that Mary never left Jesus. She stayed by His side until He commanded otherwise. All of the other disciples (except for John) ran away because they were afraid. But she did not. She remained strong and brave and stayed where she was needed.

This is one of the last examples we have of what it is to be a powerful and strong person. Jesus barely had any breath left in Him (this was one of the last 7 things He said before He died), but He used these last moments to officially give us Mary as our mother. John represents all of us who are disciples of Jesus and he is given a mother who he then takes into his home.

From this, we are given Mary to call on as our own mother and friend.

Name: _____

The Virgin Mary

1. Mary appears in the Gospel 7 times. List those 7 times:

_____   _____

_____   _____

_____   _____

_____

2. When the angel Gabriel came to Mary and explained to her that she will have a Son and that He will be the Savior of the world, what was her answer?

_____

3. When and where does Jesus give us Mary as our Mother?

_____

_____

4. If we look to Mary our Mother and ask for her guidance, who will she always lead us to?

_____

Jesus the SUN & SON
☆ ACTIVITY ☆

WHAT YOU'LL NEED:
- ☆ Scissors
- ☆ Glue Stick
- ☆ Crayons
- ☆ Pencil

INSTRUCTIONS:

1. Cut out the images of Jesus and Mary in circles.

2. On the following page, draw the sun and draw the moon (make the circles big enough to fit the cut outs inside of each).

3. Glue the image of Jesus inside the sun and glue the image of the Virgin Mary inside the moon.

Name: _____

Mary will always bring you to her Son.
He is not only the S-O-N, but also the S-U-N.
Mary is the MOON. Everything good in her is reflected off of Jesus'
radiance, goodness, and glory. Remember that you have a mom and
friend in Mary who understands your difficulties in life
because she has been there.
Call on her to bring you and your family to her Son.

CHAPTER 6

God's Field

MEMORY VERSE: 2 Peter 3:18

"But continue to grow in the grace and knowledge of our Lord and Savior Jesus Christ. To Him be the glory, now and forever! Amen."

SPIRITUAL GARDEN

In this chapter's Memory Verse, St. Peter is explaining the importance of growth. From the moment we are born, we are constantly growing. Are you as tall as you were last year? Do you weigh the same? No, because you are growing and getting stronger and bigger.

Just like we are growing on the outside, we are also growing on the inside. Our relationship with God should always be getting stronger and our faith increasing – and that's what St. Peter is talking about in this Memory Verse.

Have you ever planted flowers or vegetables in a garden? What makes the plants grow?
☆ Sunlight, water, rich soil, etc...

In this chapter, we will be exploring a different kind of garden, a spiritual garden – The Church.

The word "Church" means "to call together." Jesus "calls us together" to be His family – His Church. The Church is like a garden where different plants grow together. We are the plants God assembles together in this one spiritual garden.

For example, in the Parable of the Talents (assignment from chapter 1), we learned about how each of us has different talents that we should use for the Glory of God. That is exactly how we are all a part of the Church. Someone who sings is a rose, someone who teaches is a daisy, someone who volunteers with the elderly is an orange blossom – all of us are different, but we all make up this beautiful spiritual garden, The Church.

So if we grow on the outside (physically) by eating, sleeping, and exercising, how do we grow on the inside in our relationship with God (spiritually)? Some examples:

☆ Praying   ☆ Following God's Commandments
☆ Reading the Bible   ☆ Going to Church every Sunday

From the time you start this First Communion Journey until you are finished, you should have grown and changed. Just like every time we go to Church. We should be constantly growing in our relationship with God.

PARABLE OF THE SOWER

Open your Bible to Luke 8:4-8 to read this parable. Jesus then explains the parable in the next section – Luke 8:11-15.
☆ What is Jesus saying?
   The seed is the Word of God and we need to be sure that the seed is falling on good soil. Our hearts need to be open to God's words so that we continue to believe, no matter what. That way we grow closer to God every day.

Get seeds for planting (brown lentils work great for this activity). Prepare a small pot with potting soil and proper drainage. Throw seeds on a path, on rocks, in a thorn bush, and then finally, plant seeds in the prepared pot. Over the next week, check those same spots and see where the seeds thrived.

Go outside to see what Jesus is teaching us in the Parable of the Sower.

Throw some seeds onto a path.
> ☆ PATH = those who hear God's words but the devil takes the message away – making them not have faith.

Throw some seeds on rocks.
> ☆ ROCKS = those who hear God's words and are filled with joy. But they have no roots so when hard times come, their faith dies.

Throw some seeds into thorn bushes.
> ☆ THORN BUSHES = those who hear God's words but are more concerned with riches and pleasures in life that their faith dies.

Plant seeds in your prepared pot with the potting soil.
> ☆ RICH SOIL = those who hear God's words and have true faith and continue to believe no matter what. As a result, they grow closer to God and bear good fruit.

REMEMBER: We are all sinners and need to be in the Church. Through this parable, it is important to note that the Church is made up of different kinds of people. Some seeds fall on rocks and thorns and do not survive. They lose their faith. Not everyone is good and some will keep doing bad things even though they are in Jesus' Church. That is why it is so important to pray for each other and work hard to be the rich soil and bear good fruit for the Church.

Name: _____

God's Field

1. We grow on the outside (physically) by eating, sleeping, and exercising. How do we grow on the inside in our relationship with God (spiritually)?

_____

_____

2. What is Jesus telling us through the Parable of the Sower?

_____

_____

_____

3. What does each part of the parable stand for?

The Sower (Man Planting the Seeds): _____

The Seeds: _____

The Path: _____

_____

The Rocks: _____

_____

The Thorn Bushes: _____

_____

The Rich Soil: _____

_____

CHAPTER 7

Jesus, The Good Shepherd

MEMORY VERSE: Matthew 28:20b

"And I will be with you always, to the end of the age."

WHO IS JESUS?

In this chapter's Memory Verse, Jesus is not only talking to His disciples but also directly to us.

In chapter 4, we learned that Jesus is our friend and has all the qualities of a good friend: someone who is loyal, loving, respectful, forgiving, etc...

Again, whatever you think makes "a good and true friend," multiply that by a million and that is who Jesus is.

In Matthew 28:20b, He reassures His disciples (and us) before He goes to heaven to be with the Father, that He will never leave us and He will always be with us. NO MATTER WHAT.

THE GOOD SHEPHERD

Open your Bible to John 10:7-18 so we can further explore who Jesus is through this parable.
    In this story...
        ☆Who are the sheep? GOD'S CHILDREN
        ☆Who is the Shepherd? JESUS
        ☆Who is the wolf? THE DEVIL
        ☆Who is the hired man? EVIL THAT COMES FROM THE DEVIL – People that pretend to be our shepherd but they do not really love or care for us.

☆According to Jesus, what does a good shepherd do? Lay down his life for his sheep.
☆What does this mean? A good shepherd would risk his own life just to protect the sheep.
☆What does the hired man do when a wolf comes? Runs the other way leaving the sheep behind because he does not care.
☆What happens to a flock of sheep if there is no shepherd? They scatter and can be easily attacked by a wolf.

Does the good shepherd know His sheep? Do the sheep know their shepherd? YES!

Open your Bible to John 10:10b and read that verse again.
    What is Jesus saying to us in this passage? Why did He come?
Read John 10:18 again.
    Jesus came to save us and if we follow God's commands just as Jesus did, we will live life to the fullest. He came to save us, protect us, and He will always be there for us – He is the Good Shepherd and our greatest friend.

Name: _____

Jesus, the Good Shepherd

1. What does each part of the parable stand for?

The Shepherd: _____

The Sheep: _____

The Wolf: _____

The Hired Man: _____

_____

2. What does a Good Shepherd do? How is Jesus the Good Shepherd?

_____

_____

_____

3. Jesus came so that we can have life in its fullness. How can we have that through Him?

_____

_____

_____

_____

TURN THE PAGE!

Jesus, the Good Shepherd

Help guide the sheep back to Jesus and stay far away from the wolf.

LOST

FOUND

CHAPTER 8

The Church, One Body

OUR BODIES ARE WONDERFULLY MADE

Take a look at Memory Verse #1 in this chapter. In this verse, King David is praising God for how perfectly He made our bodies. God took so much care in making each and every one of us and He loves us so very much.

Can you touch your nose? How about your mouth, ears, arms, or feet? These are all parts of your body and each part is important. They all work together to make your body function properly. For example, your eyes help your body see where you are going, and your feet help you get there. Your stomach tells you when you are hungry, and your hands help feed your mouth so that you can be full again.

Open your Bible to Psalm 139:13-16 to continue reading what King David wrote.

God made us all very, very special!

THE CHURCH IS THE BODY OF CHRIST

What is the "Church?" The "Church" is all the people who believe in Jesus and have been baptized in Him.

The Church is called the "Body of Christ" and Jesus is the Head of that Body.

Just like our bodies have life in them through our soul, the Church is a living Body because the Holy Spirit gives it life. He is the Soul of the Body of Christ.

WE ARE ALL DIFFERENT

Our bodies are wonderfully made and have many different parts that work so well together. In the same way, the Church is made up of lots of parts. Each of us is part of the Church, the Body of Christ.

What if the body did not have different parts? What if your body was made up of 25 eyeballs? You would be able to see really well, but you would not be able to do anything else. Our bodies have to have different parts that work together to function properly.

We each have our different gifts that God has given us . God wants us to use our different gifts and talents to continue to build up the Body of Christ.

This means working together and caring for one another because we are all connected as one Body. For example, if your hand is broken, it is not just your one hand that gets affected. Your other hand might have to work harder. It might affect how you use your feet or mouth. Your brain might even have to think in a different way in order to get things done.

So what does this mean for the Body of Christ?
- ☆**First:** You need to make sure that you keep a happy and healthy relationship with Jesus so that you are a good and functional member of the Body of Christ.
- ☆**Second:** If you see a fellow member suffering or failing, it is your responsibility to help and support that member.

REMEMBER: Just like our physical bodies are connected, in the Body of Christ we are all connected to each other as well. It is our responsibility to make sure that the Body of Christ remains healthy and strong.

Open your Bible to 1 Corinthians 12:12-27 (up to Memory Verse #2):

St. Paul is specifically telling us that, as members of the Body of Christ, we are all equally important. Each of us has a different function. And because of that, we must continue to work together to build that Body with grace and joy.

The Church, One Body

1. Who is the Head of the Church?

_____

2. Just like our physical bodies have many different parts, the Body of Christ also has many different parts. Who are the different parts?

_____

_____

_____

3. Read 1 Corinthians 12:12-26. What is the St. Paul saying about the different parts of the Body of Christ?

_____

_____

_____

_____

_____

_____

My Family & The Church
⭐ ACTIVITY ⭐

WHAT YOU'LL NEED:
- ⭐Colorful Construction Paper
- ⭐Scissors
- ⭐Glue Stick
- ⭐Crayons
- ⭐4x6 Picture of Your Family

INSTRUCTIONS:

1. Color the inserts for the inside of the Church doors and cut out along lines.

2. Color heading and cut out along line.

3. Color the front of the Church. Cut out along the outside lines. Flip the Church over and color the back sides of the doors (these will show later on).

4. Choose your favorite family photo (4x6 size).

5. On a piece of construction paper, glue the heading to the top of the paper.

6. Cut the Church doors along the dotted lines. Fold each door back on the solid line so that they can open and close.

7. Glue the inserts for inside of the Church doors - one on each door so you can see them once the doors open.

8. Glue the 4x6 family photo towards the bottom middle of the construction paper.

9. Glue the Church on top of the photo so that once the doors of the Church are opened, you can see your family inside.

We are all different parts of the Body of Christ!

"Christ is like a single body, which has many parts; it is still one body, even though it is made up of different parts."

1 Corinthians 12:12

INSERTS FOR INSIDE OF CHURCH DOORS

One Body, Many Parts

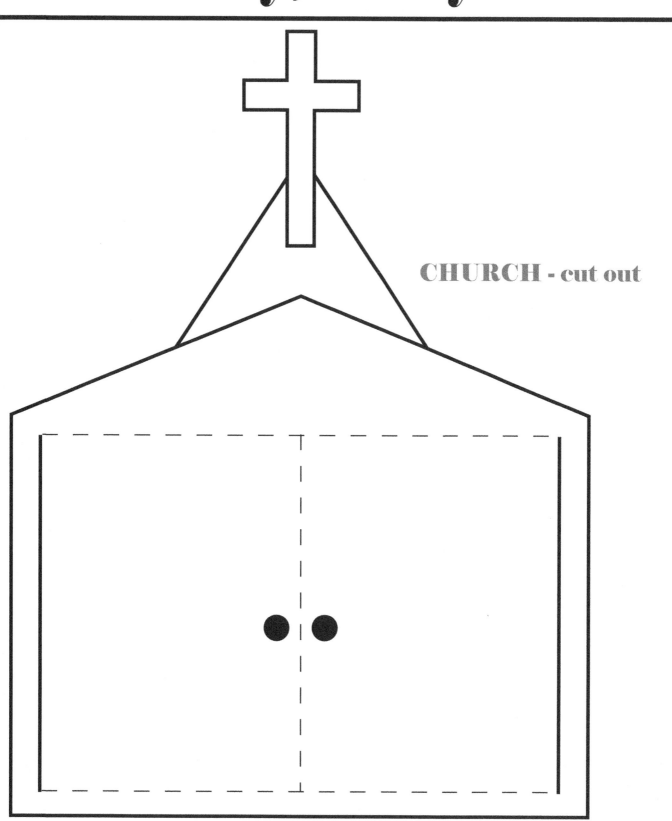

CHAPTER 9

Church Organization

THE IMPORTANCE OF OUR CHURCH

In the last chapter, we explained that the Church is One Body, Jesus is the Head of the Church, and we (the different members) make up the Body.

Where do the member of the Body of Christ come together?
    ☆In our Churches!

In this chapter's Memory Verse, Matthew 18:20, Jesus is saying where two or more are gathered in His name, He is with us. Where do we gather in His name?
    ☆In our Churches!

Isn't it amazing to know that He is with us in Church when we gather together? That is why it is so important for us to have a Church and for us to gather in His name. This keeps the Body of Christ alive and strong.

CHURCH STRUCTURE

In the same way our homes and families have a certain order (with someone in charge) our Church also has a set structure.

Open your Bible to Matthew 16:13-19 to see where this structure originally came from.
    ☆In these verses, Jesus is setting up the structure of the Church and appointing the Church's first pope – St. Peter.

St. Peter was an ordinary man. He was a poor fisherman who had a family. But what made him extraordinary was his faith and fire. Jesus saw in him these qualities and put him in charge to lead the people after His resurrection.

We often look at these saints and popes and think that they are so different from us. But it is not necessarily true. Peter was not a king or a powerful, rich man in his village. And it is not an accident that Jesus chose an ordinary, poor fisherman to lead something as big and important as His Church.

Jesus is showing us that faith makes ordinary, extraordinary. He gave the biggest titles to ordinary people to show us that with faith and Him in our hearts we can do ANYTHING.

Take comfort in knowing that your faith can do extraordinary things. There very well could be a future nun, priest, or even pope reading these words!

CHURCH STRUCTURE:

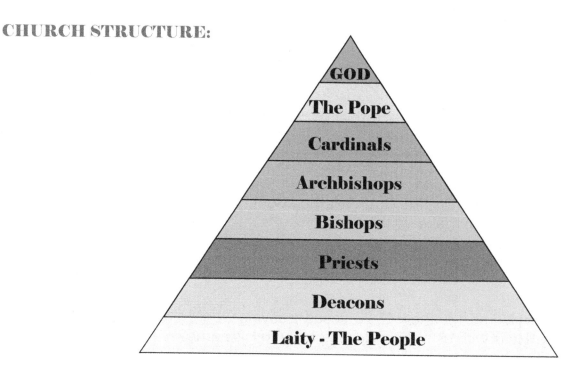

God is, of course, the head of the Church and we believe that all the decisions that have been made after Jesus left us have been guided by the Holy Spirit. The pope is in charge here on earth. The cardinals, archbishops, bishops, priests, and deacons then follow.

☆ Can you name the bishop of your diocese?
☆ Can you name the priest(s) of your parish?
☆ Can you name the deacon(s) of your parish?

All of the people that you named are assigned to your parish and fit into this Church structure.

There is one final group: the laity, which is you!

HOW CAN YOU HELP?

The biggest part of this pyramid structure is you. Now unless you receive a very special calling from God to be a nun, deacon, priest, bishop, or even pope, you will remain in this group. As the laity, there are so many ways you can help make the Body of Christ strong and keep it healthy.

God calls upon us in so many different ways – not just to be priests or nuns. While those are very special callings, did you know that, for example, your father and mother had a very special calling as well? To be a mother or father and raise children into the Body of Christ is a BIG calling. When your parents got married, their job as husband and wife became to love God first, then love each other, and then have children which they love and raise into the faith. You are reading this book and preparing for your First Communion because your parents are obeying God in this really beautiful calling.

But it does not end there. There are so many ways you can volunteer within the Church and follow other callings in your life. Here are some examples:

☆ Altar Server
☆ Lector (those who read the Bible Reading for Holy Mass)

☆ Choir Member
☆ Religious Education Teacher

THE MOST IMPORTANT WAY YOU CAN HELP

Again, just because we are not nuns or priests, does not mean we cannot make a BIG impact in our world. We are followers of Jesus. Everything we do should reflect that.

For example, if you are at school and see someone hurt or crying, BECAUSE you are a follower of Jesus, you have to think: what would Jesus do in this moment?

What would He do?

☆He would be kind to them and lovingly help them. And we should do the same. So when people see how we treat EVERYONE with love, compassion, and kindness, they will know that there is something very special about us – and that something special is Jesus.

Think of it in the opposite way. If you saw someone at school hurt or crying, and you run over and make fun of them, what would someone who knows you are a follower of Jesus think? They would think there is something very wrong with your actions and you may even make someone question what it is to be a follower of Jesus.

☆ALWAYS know that your actions toward each other are the biggest and best ways to build up the Body of Christ – when you are good, kind, and loving, you can inspire people around you to do the same.

———————————— ☆ ACTIVITY ☆ ————————————

During this week, find an opportunity to do a random act of kindness for someone. Whether it is a big act or small, if you know this person or not, does not matter. We just want to find ways to be the light of Jesus for others to see and build up the Body of Christ!
Write down your random act on the below lines.

_____

_____

_____

_____

_____

_____

Name: _____

Church Organization

1. Who created the Church structure and appointed the first pope?

_____

2. Who was the first pope?

_____

3. Who is the current pope?

_____

4. As part of the "Laity" in the Church, what are ways you can get involved to keep the Body of Christ alive?

_____

_____

_____

_____

_____

_____

CHAPTER 10

The Holy Mass

MEMORY VERSE: Romans 10:17

"So then, faith comes from hearing the message, and the message comes through preaching Christ."

THE HOLY MASS AND ITS IMPORTANCE

Remember when we learned about how we talk to God and how God talks to us?

☆ How do we talk to God? Through prayer.

☆ How does God talk to us? Through the Bible.

☆ Where can we pray, read the Bible, and hear the message of Christ preached all in one place? HOLY MASS!

In our Memory Verse for this chapter, St. Paul is explaining that our faith is strengthened through hearing the message of Christ.

It is so important that we attend Holy Mass not only every Sunday (that is mandatory), but as often as possible because that is how we strengthen our relationship with God.

How can Holy Mass strengthen your relationship with God? Do you have friends or cousins that do not live close to you (in another state or country)? Do you have friends or cousins that live close by that you see all the time? Even though you may love your friends and cousins that live in another state or country, you are most likely to have a stronger relationship with the ones that you see on a regular basis. You spend more time with them, you make more memories, and you become closer for that reason.

The same goes for our relationship with God. We become closer to Him when we spend more time with Him – celebrating the Holy Mass in His Home, where He is fully present. And that is all God wants. He is there waiting in EVERY Holy Mass wanting to be closer to us.

PREPARING YOURSELF FOR HOLY MASS

Holy Mass is not just an hour on Sunday we go to and leave. It is so much more than that!

First, we need to fast (no eating or drinking) one hour before Holy Mass to prepare ourselves to receive Holy Communion. The reason we do this is to basically cleanse and prepare ourselves for the presence of Jesus into our body and soul. Fasting also separates us from worldly things – bringing us closer to God.

Second, we have to make sure we are appropriately dressed. If you were going to the beach, would you go in your long sleeve pajamas? No, you would wear a bathing suit! If you were going to visit the pope, would you go see him in your bathing suit? No, you would wear the nicest things you own to meet with him.

So, if the pope deserves your nicest clothes, doesn't God deserve the very best? We should come to His home, to be in His presence, wearing proper and appropriate clothes.

DRESSING APPROPRIATELY FOR CHURCH

"Don't you know that your body is the temple of the Holy Spirit, who lives in you and who was given to you by God? You do not belong to yourselves but to God; He bought you for a price. So use your bodies for God's glory."
1 Corinthians 6:19-20

WHAT TO WEAR			WHAT NOT TO WEAR		
Short Sleeve T-Shirts, Blouses, and Polos	Short Sleeve or Long Sleeve Button Up Shirts	Office Attire	Low Waist Pants or Ripped Jeans	Sleeveless shirts, plunging necklines, or anything strapless	Short Skirts
Long Pants	Knee Length or Long Dresses with Sleeves	Knee Length or Long Skirts / Shoes	Shorts of Any Kind	Flip Flops or Any Kind of Slippers	Caps or Hats

GOING INTO CHURCH

Once you enter the Church, make the sign of the cross with the holy water at the door – this reminds us of the promise we made at our baptism as children of God.

It is VERY IMPORTANT that we arrive to Church before Holy Mass starts.

Every time you walk into the Church you must bow in front of the altar. This is out of respect for the real presence of Jesus kept safe in the tabernacle (most tabernacles are locked!).

Once you arrive to where you will sit, kneel and greet God. Just like how you go to someone's house – you walk in with love and respect and greet them. It is the same when you walk into the House of God.

While you are kneeling down before Jesus, give Him your intentions. Whatever it is you are feeling, hoping for, or anything that may be bothering you, this is the time to give it to Jesus.

Remember the chapter about our Guardian Angels? They will be attending Holy Mass with you and will take your intentions to Jesus.

WHAT HAPPENS DURING HOLY MASS?

Do you know what we are celebrating during Holy Mass?
* ☆ Throughout Holy Mass we are raising praise to the Father, through the Son, in the Holy Spirit and celebrating the Life, Death, and Resurrection of Jesus.
* ☆ We read about His life and teachings during the readings and the Gospel (He is present in the Word!)

After the priest reads the Gospel, he talks to the congregation (all of us) in order to explain the readings and relate them to our lives. This is called a homily.

Then we recite the Creed. What are we proclaiming in the Creed?
* ☆ Who God the Father is – who God the Son is – who God the Holy Spirit is – and what we believe!

Then comes the offering. This is when the collection is taken and we have an opportunity to give 10% of what we have (one of the 3T's – treasure).

Some parishioners are chosen to take the bread, wine, and collection to the priest at the altar – NOTE: at this time the bread and wine are JUST bread and wine. They are not holy yet.

The next part of the mass is the most important part – CONSECRATION.
Open your Bible to Luke 22:19-20.
* ☆ The words that the priest recites are taken from these passages that Jesus said at the Last Supper.

This is why we go to Holy Mass – to receive the REAL presence of Jesus. The first part of the Consecration is the bread changing to the Body of Christ. The second part is the wine changing to the Blood of Christ. We kneel as we hear these words because that is when our Lord becomes present.

We then say the Our Father all together and offer peace to one another. At this time it is important to make sure we are at peace with ourselves and with each other. This is not just a hand motion – we must forgive each other in order to be worthy of receiving the Body of Christ.

Then we participate in the most beautiful part of the Holy Mass – we get to receive Jesus' Body and Blood. We become as close as possible to our Lord.

St. Augustine would tell people before receiving Holy Communion, "Become what you receive."
* ☆ What does that mean? You are about to receive Jesus into your body and soul – become what you receive. Do your very best to be just like our Lord Jesus.

After you receive Holy Communion you must go back to your seat and kneel – thanking God for the opportunity to participate in this amazing celebration and all the other blessings in your life.

It is very important you stay until the very end to receive the final blessing. At this time the priest blesses all the congregation and we are dismissed to go in Jesus' peace.

The Holy Mass

1. What is the best way to strengthen our relationship with God?

_____

_____

2. Why do we fast one hour before receiving Holy Communion?

_____

_____

_____

3. According to the dress code chart, circle yes or no if the items of clothing listed below are appropriate for Church:

Shorts: YES   NO   Pants: YES   NO

Polo Shirts: YES   NO   Slippers: YES   NO

4. Why should we arrive to Church before Holy Mass starts?

_____

_____

_____

5. What are we celebrating during Holy Mass?

_____

_____

6. What happens during Consecration?

_____

_____

_____

_____

7. Why is it important to offer our intentions to God?

_____

_____

_____

8. What did St. Augustine mean when he said "Become what you receive" as he gave Holy Communion?

_____

_____

_____

_____

Name: _____

The Holy Mass
Crossword Puzzle

DOWN

1. We have to make sure we are appropriately _____.

2. Holy water at the door reminds us of the promise we made at our _____ as children of God.

3. Every time you walk into the church you must _____ in front of the altar.

4. Your Guardian _____ attends Holy Mass with you.

5. The priest gives a _____ after reading the Gospel.

6. During the _____, we are proclaiming who God the Father is, who God the Son is, who God the Holy Spirit is, and what we believe!

7. The offering is when we can give 10% of our _____ to the Church (one of the 3T's!).

8. During Consecration, the wine turns into the _____ of Christ.

9. St. Augustine would tell people before receiving communion, "Become what you _____."

10. It is very important to stay until the end of Holy Mass to receive the ____ blessing.

ACROSS

1. During Holy _____ we can pray, read the Bible, and hear the message of Christ.

2. We need to _____ (no eating or drinking) one hour before mass to prepare ourselves to receive Holy Communion.

3. During Consecration the bread turns into the _____ of Christ.

4. When you enter Church and kneel down before Jesus, give Him your _____.

5. When did Jesus say the words said during Consecration?

6. Holy Mass is a _____.

CHAPTER 11

Faith, Hope, & Love

MEMORY VERSE: 1 Corinthians 13:13

"Meanwhile these three remain: faith, hope, and love; and the greatest of these is love."

THESE THREE REMAIN

Take a look at the above Memory Verse. Faith, Hope, and Love are so important to our Christianity that St. Paul made sure to highlight them throughout 1 Corinthians, Chapter 13. Let us dig a little deeper in order to learn the meaning of each.

FAITH

What is Faith?
☆Faith is the complete trust or confidence in someone or something.

The opposite of faith is fear. So when we have COMPLETE confidence and trust in someone, we are not afraid – we have faith in them.

Is there someone in your life that you have complete trust, confidence, or faith in? Above anyone else, even above your parents, you should have complete faith in God. God throughout the Bible shows us that we should never be afraid and that we should always put our faith in Him. He will NEVER fail us.

Open your Bible to the below passages and read each one:
☆Genesis 15:1	☆Isaiah 41:10	☆Mark 5:36
☆Deuteronomy 31:8	☆Matthew 28:10	☆Luke 1:30

What do all these verses have in common? "**DO NOT BE AFRAID.**"

☆Do you know how many times "Do not be afraid" is in the Bible? 365
☆How many days are in a year? 365
☆God has placed a "Do not be afraid" in the Bible for every day of the year!

When we let fear come into our hearts it slowly chips away at our faith. When this happens, it is as if we are telling God that we do not trust Him.

Open your Bible to Matthew 14:22-33.
Jesus told Peter to come, and he did. And he was ACTUALLY walking on water. No one but Jesus had ever done that. Peter, through his faith in Jesus, walked on water! But what happened next? He became afraid and slowly began to sink. At once, Jesus pulled him out and saved him, explaining that if he had more faith and less fear, he would not have almost drowned.

This happens to us all the time. We are so worried and anxious about the little things in life, that we forget that God has a wonderful plan for each of us. So we should never fear.

HOPE

What is Hope?

☆Hope is to want something to happen or be true.

Faith and hope are different but they are tied together. In Hebrews 11:1, St. Paul says, "To have faith is to be sure of the things we hope for, to be certain of the things we cannot see." When we have hope we will not give up on our faith – our hope increases our faith.

Open your Bible to Matthew 8:5-13.

☆The prayer, "Lord I am not worthy that you should enter under my roof, but only say the word and my soul shall be healed" which is said in most Catholic masses, comes from these verses.

☆The Centurion hoped that his servant would get better, and that hope fueled his faith in Jesus. Even Jesus was amazed at the hope and faith that this man had.

There is also a bigger kind of hope that fuels our faith in being followers of Jesus. That is the hope in the Resurrection.

Why did Jesus come to this earth?

☆Remember the Memory Verse from Chapter 1? God loved the world so much that He sent His only Son to die for our sins. So if Jesus came to die for our sins, what does that mean? He has conquered death!

In John 16:33, Jesus says, "I have told you this so that you will have peace by being united to me. The world will make you suffer. But be brave! I have defeated the world!" He gives us peace because no matter what happens in this life, it does not matter. Our hope is in the Resurrection and in knowing that if we are followers of Jesus, we will be in heaven with Him one day. Have you had someone close to you pass away? As sad as it may be to lose someone because we will miss them here, Jesus has given us HOPE in His Resurrection, that we will be with them again one day. And it will be forever, in heaven.

LOVE

What is Love?

☆So far, we have reviewed a lot regarding what the Bible says love is.

But St. Paul specifically says, "the GREATEST of these is love." Why do you think? The entire Bible is one big love story. In the beginning, God created Adam and Eve so He can share the world with them. But as they fell away from Him and people continued to do bad things, His plan was to send His Son to save us so that we can live with Him in heaven one day.

Everything God does is simply out of His pure love for us.

Open your Bible to John 15:13.
  ☆ Jesus makes it even more clear about the greatest love of all. The sacrifice Jesus made for all of us (the suffering He went through, his friends abandoning Him, everyone making fun of Him, the crucifixion) is the GREATEST form of love.

And since God loves us so much, we should then pass that love on to one another.

Open your Bible to John 13:34.
  ☆ What is Jesus commanding us to do? "Love one another as I have loved you."
  ☆ What does that mean? How did Jesus show His love?

Everything Jesus did was out of His love for God the Father and His love for us. He taught with kindness and patience, healed those who needed it, felt pity for those who needed His help, and, most of all, He died for us.

So, what are some examples of how we can show our love for one another?
  ☆ Be kind   ☆ Be helpful   ☆ Be a good friend

  ☆ Be compassionate – if someone is hurt or needs help, be there for them

In showing love for each other, we are showing Jesus how much we love Him as well.

———————————— ☆ ACTIVITY ☆ ————————————

Color each symbol and write down what each means to you.

_____   _____   _____

_____   _____   _____

_____   _____   _____

_____   _____   _____

Faith, Hope, & Love

1. Of Faith, Hope, & Love, which does St. Paul say is the greatest?

_____

2. How many times is "Do Not be Afraid" repeated in the Bible?

_____

3. What do we learn about Faith from the story about Peter walking on water?

_____

_____

_____

_____

4. Fear is good for our faith.   TRUE   or   FALSE

5. Having hope increases our faith.   TRUE   or   FALSE

6. What does it mean to have Hope in the Resurrection?

_____

_____

_____

TURN THE PAGE!

7. In John 13:34, what is Jesus commanding us to do?

_____

_____

8. How can we show our love for each other?

_____

_____

_____

_____

_____

CHAPTER 12

Discipleship

WHAT IS A DISCIPLE?

A disciple is a follower or student of a teacher. Jesus was the greatest teacher of all time and he had 12 original disciples that followed Him and learned from Him:

☆(Simon) Peter	☆John	☆Simon	☆Philip
☆Thomas	☆Andrew	☆Bartholomew	☆James
☆Matthew	☆James the Less	☆Jude	☆Judas

THE CALLING OF (SIMON) PETER

Open your Bible to Luke 5:1-11.

☆What is happening in this story?
Jesus performed this amazing miracle which caused Simon Peter, James, and John to leave everything and follow Him.

☆What is happening in verse 5?
Simon Peter is explaining to Jesus that they already cast their nets and caught nothing. But if Jesus wants them to, they will cast the nets again.

Once Simon Peter cast down the nets, he caught so many fish that the nets began to burst! When he saw this, Simon Peter felt the greatness of Jesus' presence and felt the weight of his own sin. For this reason he says, "Go away from me, Lord! I am a sinful man!"

This is like when your mom or dad treats you so well and you are either not being nice, have lied, or done something wrong. You feel bad and ashamed that someone is so good to you even though you do not necessarily deserve it.

That is what Simon Peter felt.

Jesus is also showing Simon Peter that his life without Jesus is an empty net. But his life with Jesus is not just full, it is over flowing with blessings. Jesus again says, "**DO NOT BE AFRAID** – from now on, you will be catching people."

They will no longer be catching fish, from now on they will be catching people – which means they will be introducing people to Jesus and bringing them into the faith as His disciples.

THE POWER OF FAITH IN DISCIPLESHIP
Open your Bible to John 14:12.

What did Jesus "do?" His miracles – healing of the sick, making blind people see, calming of the storm, and so many other amazing miracles. But what was Jesus' greatest miracle? The Resurrection! Jesus rising from the dead was His most amazing miracle and the reason for our hope in this world. Because of this incredible miracle, for over 2,000 years until now, those who believe in Jesus can have eternal life in heaven with Him.

From this we can learn that the greatest miracle of all is bringing sinners to Jesus so we can all be in heaven together.

MIRACLE OF PETER
Some perfect examples of this are the miracles that happened after Jesus left this earth.

Jesus commanded the disciples to preach His Word to all nations after His Ascension into heaven. While teaching the people about Jesus and baptizing them in His name, they also performed miracles in His name. This led even more people to believe.

Open your Bible to Acts 9:32-35.
   ☆What happens in these verses?
     Peter healed a crippled man! After seeing this, ALL the people in the village believed in the Lord.

That is the power of faith and the power of discipleship.

Because of Peter's discipleship and strong faith in Jesus, he made all these people turn to Jesus and follow Him as well. These people are now saved by Jesus because of Peter's faith. How amazing is that!

SO WHAT DOES THAT MEAN FOR US?
Take a look at our Memory Verse for this chapter.

Jesus is giving us His last commandment. It is a call to be active.

As followers of Jesus we have been given a big responsibility. When we were baptized, we were given this light. It is our responsibility to keep that light bright and shine it for others around us to see.

So even if we are not healing people that are sick or making blind people see, we are still being active disciples by the way we live our lives. If you are kind and spread love to everyone around you, you are doing Jesus' work

In a world that has so much darkness and sadness, let God's light shine through your love and kindness. That light shining bright is what makes you different. You never know who your kindness and love can be saving and bringing to Jesus.

Name: _____

Discipleship

1. Who were the original 12 Disciples of Jesus?

_____   _____

_____   _____

_____   _____

_____   _____

_____   _____

2. In Luke 5:10, what did Jesus say to Peter?

_____

_____

3. What does Jesus mean when he says "you will be catching people?"

_____

_____

TURN THE PAGE!

4. How can we be active disciples of Jesus?

_____

_____

_____

_____

_____

_____

_____

_____

Fishers of Men!
⭐ ACTIVITY ⭐

WHAT YOU'LL NEED:
- ⭐ Scissors
- ⭐ Crayons
- ⭐ Drinking Straw
- ⭐ Stapler
- ⭐ Yarn or String

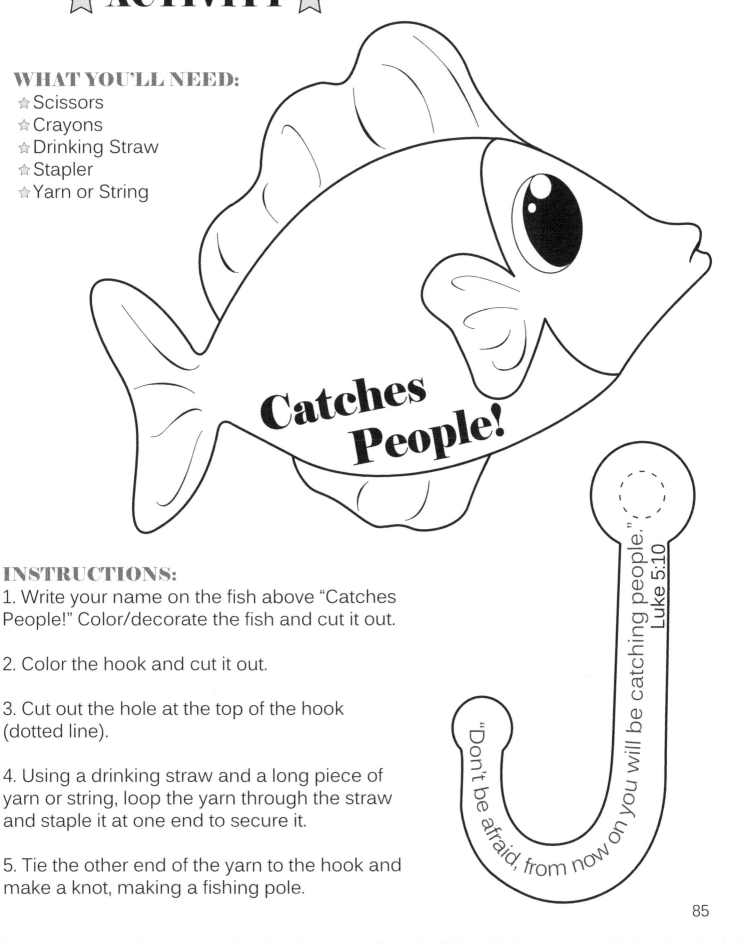

Catches People!

"Don't be afraid, from now on you will be catching people." Luke 5:10

INSTRUCTIONS:

1. Write your name on the fish above "Catches People!" Color/decorate the fish and cut it out.

2. Color the hook and cut it out.

3. Cut out the hole at the top of the hook (dotted line).

4. Using a drinking straw and a long piece of yarn or string, loop the yarn through the straw and staple it at one end to secure it.

5. Tie the other end of the yarn to the hook and make a knot, making a fishing pole.

CHAPTER 13

The Seven Sacraments

MEMORY VERSE: Ephesians 2:8-9

"For it is by God's grace that you have been saved through faith. It is not the result of your own efforts, but God's gift, so that no one can boast about it."

WHAT IS A SACRAMENT?

A Sacrament is a visible sign of an invisible grace that is given by God.

In this chapter's Memory Verse, St. Paul is talking about how we have been saved – by grace through faith.

☆ What is grace?

Example -- Imagine if someone keeps lying to you, does things to hurt you, and is not being a very good person. But despite all of this person's actions, you keep loving them, forgiving them, and sending them help whenever they need it.

That is the grace of God. God's grace throughout the entire Bible refers to how even when we did not deserve it (because we are sinners and do bad things), God still loves us, protects us, forgives us, and has sent His only Son as our Savior. Therefore, we are saved by His grace and through our faith in Him.

What does that mean in the Sacraments? The Sacraments are ways in which God shares His Kingdom with us (the Church!) on earth. They allow us to partake in an invisible grace through a visible sign.

THE SEVEN SACRAMENTS

Baptism: The priest cleanses you from your original sin to become a member of the Body of Christ. **Grace:** Makes you a child of God **Sign:** Washing with Holy Water in the name of the Father, Son, and the Holy Spirit	**Confirmation:** This is when we receive the gift of the Holy Spirit. We are anointed with Holy Oil (Chrism) and sent forth to make disciples for Jesus. **Grace:** God gives you all the gifts of the Holy Spirit **Sign:** Blessing with Holy Oil called "Chrism"
Confession: Through a priest, God gives you the great gift of forgiveness. **Grace:** God gives you His forgiveness **Sign:** Priest's words of comfort and absolution	**Holy Communion:** During consecration, the bread and wine turn into the real Body and Blood of Christ for you to receive during mass. **Grace:** Jesus gives you His Body and Blood **Sign:** Bread and wine
Matrimony: The union between a man and woman in the Church through God. **Grace:** Makes holy the love between a man and a woman **Sign:** Blessing and Crowns	**Holy Orders:** This special Sacrament is for the men who have been called to become a deacon, priest, or bishop. **Grace:** Consecrates a man's life to serve Jesus **Sign:** Prayer of consecration and anointing by the Bishop with the Oil of the Messiah
Anointing of the Sick: A priest will anoint someone who is very ill with Holy Oil (Chrism). This strengthens them and unites their suffering with the suffering of Christ on the cross. **Grace:** Offers God's help to the sick **Sign:** Blessing with Oil	

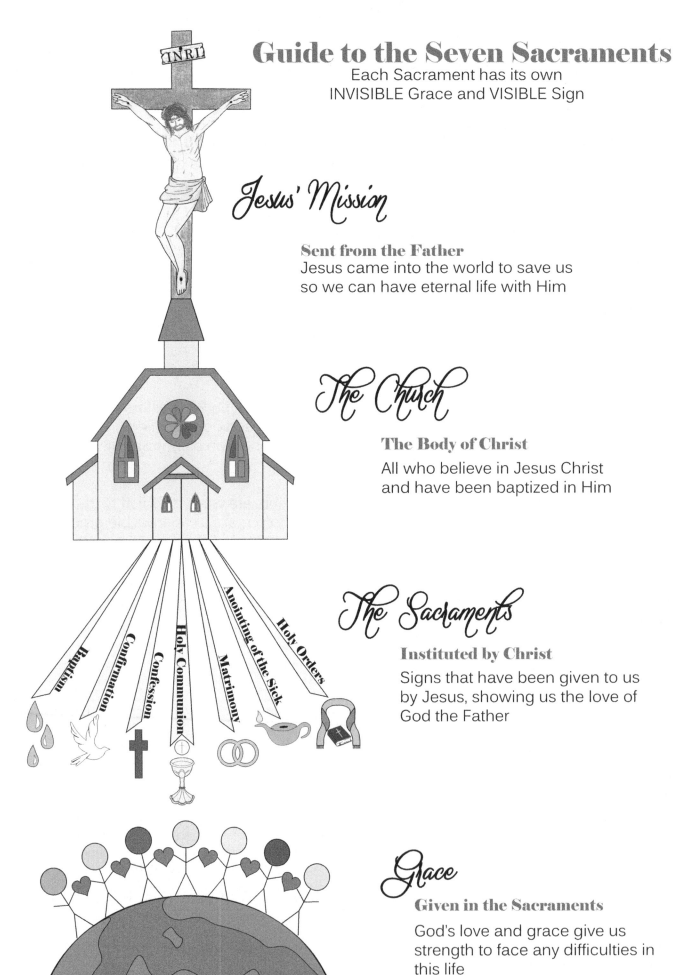

Guide to the Seven Sacraments
Each Sacrament has its own
INVISIBLE Grace and VISIBLE Sign

Jesus' Mission

Sent from the Father
Jesus came into the world to save us
so we can have eternal life with Him

The Church

The Body of Christ
All who believe in Jesus Christ
and have been baptized in Him

The Sacraments

Instituted by Christ
Signs that have been given to us
by Jesus, showing us the love of
God the Father

Baptism

Confirmation

Confession

Holy Communion

Matrimony

Anointing of the Sick

Holy Orders

Grace

Given in the Sacraments
God's love and grace give us
strength to face any difficulties in
this life

The Seven Sacraments

1. A sacrament is a _____ sign of an _____

Grace that is given by God.

2. What are the 7 Sacraments?

_____   _____

_____   _____

_____   _____

_____

3. Why did Jesus come into the world?

_____

_____

_____

4. Each Sacrament has a grace and a sign. List the grace and sign for the Sacrament of Baptism:

_____

_____

5. Each Sacrament has a grace and a sign. List the grace and sign for the Sacrament of Matrimony:

_____

_____

6. What does the Memory Verse, Ephesians 2:8-9, say about grace and faith?

_____

_____

_____

_____

_____

_____

_____

HOLY ORDER

Grace: Makes you a child of God

Sign: Washing with Holy Water in the name of the Father, and the Son, and the Holy Spirit

Match Game
⭐ ACTIVITY ⭐

1. Using scissors, cut out each square.

2. Mix up the squares and place them face down in rows.

3. Turn over any two cards (one at a time) and try to find the Sacrament that matches the grace and sign.

HOLY COMMUNION

Grace: God gives you His forgiveness

Sign: Priest's words of comfort and absolution

MATRIMONY

Grace: Jesus gives you His Body and Blood

Sign: Bread and wine

BAPTISM

Grace: Makes holy the love between a man and a woman

Sign: Blessing and Crowns

CONFIRMATION

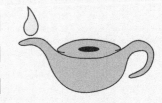

Grace: Offers God's help to the sick

Sign: Blessing with Oil

CONFESSION

Grace: Consecrates a man's life to serve Jesus

Sign: Prayer of consecration and anointing with oil by the Bishop

ANOINTING OF THE SICK

Grace: God gives you all the gifts of the Holy Spirit

Sign: Blessing with Holy Oil called "Chrism"

The Ten Commandments

WHAT IS A COMMANDMENT?

A commandment is a rule we need to live by and follow.

Take a look at the Memory Verse for this chapter. Jesus is blessing all of those who follow God's commandments. Which means that we will be blessed if we follow His rules!

The original rules that Moses received from God are called The Ten Commandments.

Let us dive deeper into each commandment in order to understand what they mean.

THE TEN COMMANDMENTS

Open your Bible to where the Ten Commandments are and read them – Exodus 20:1-17

1. I am the Lord your God. You shall not have strange gods before me.

This is the first commandment because it is the most important one! God must be first in our lives. NOTHING should come before Him. In the time of Moses, God was telling them to not worship any false idols because that is what the Egyptians before them did (they would worship animals like cows or goats). Today, we may not be worshiping cows or goats, but we still put other things before God. Whether it be our school, our hobbies, or other things we enjoy, we sometimes make them a priority over God who is our Creator and loves us the most. He should always come first.

2. You shall not take the name of the Lord your God in vain.

God should only be called on in praise, love, and for our intentions. His name should remain holy. This commandment is also about our language in general. We should not use foul language and we should always be mindful of the words that come out of our mouths.

3. Remember to keep holy the Lord's day.

What day is the "Lord's day?" SUNDAY! We must keep Sunday holy which means to attend Holy Mass every Sunday. Arrive on time, be respectful, and pay attention during Holy Mass.

4. Honor your father and your mother.

God is commanding us to respect and obey our parents. This includes being helpful without complaining and being a good example if you have siblings. This is also meant for authority figures who are not your parents – priests, nuns, teachers, older people, etc...

5. You shall not kill.

We should never harm anyone physically. But this is not just about hurting or killing someone on the outside. Do you know that this commandment is also about hurting someone on the inside? You should not say mean things or make fun of others as this is a form of killing people on the inside. That is why it is so important to be loving to everyone you encounter.

6. You shall not commit adultery.

When you are married, you should always be faithful and truthful to your husband or wife. Treat your bodies with purity and respect. Be modest in your behavior and in the way you dress. This also includes keeping yourselves pure for the person you will marry one day.

7. You shall not steal.

Do not take things that are not yours without being allowed to do so. Do not destroy or misuse another person's property and always return the things you borrow.

8. You shall not bear false witness.

ALWAYS be truthful.

9. You shall not covet your neighbor's wife.

Do not be jealous. Be pure in thoughts and in desires, treating all people with love and respect.

10. You shall not covet your neighbor's goods.

Do not be jealous. Be satisfied with your own things. Be thankful to God and your parents for what they have given you. Share your things with others.

Did you notice something interesting? Every commandment is about a different topic, except for the last two. The last two commandments are about the same topic, jealousy. Jealousy is such an ugly sin that can ruin so much good around us and take away our joy.

Open your Bible to James 3:14-15.
   ☆ What is St. James saying about jealousy? It is ugly and from this world. He even says "demonic." This is not an emotion that comes from God and we have to be very careful to guard our hearts from it.

The best way to do this is to be THANKFUL for all that God has blessed us with. Focus on that and not what others around us have.

Name: _____

The Ten Commandments

1. In which book of the Bible can the Ten Commandments be found?

_____

2. Who were the original Ten Commandments given to?

_____

3. How can we obey the 1st Commandment?

_____

_____

4. Which day of the week is the "Lord's day"?

_____

5. The 5th Commandment is ONLY about physically killing someone. (circle one)

TRUE   or   FALSE

6. What does the 8th Commandment mean?

_____

TURN THE PAGE!

7. What are the 9th and 10th commandments about?

_____

8. In James 3:14-15, what is St. James saying about jealousy? What is the best way to guard your heart from jealousy?

_____

_____

_____

_____

_____

_____

_____

10 Commandments
⭐ ACTIVITY ⭐

WHAT YOU'LL NEED:
☆ Scissors
☆ Crayons
☆ Markers
☆ Glue Stick
☆ Colorful Construction Paper

INSTRUCTIONS:

1. Color each tablet on the front and the reverse sides of the page.
2. Cut out each tablet.
3. Fold each tablet closed on the dotted lines.
4. Write the number of each commandment with a marker on the folded front of each tablet.
5. Glue the folded tablets onto a piece of construction paper – leaving the folded flaps accessible to easily open and close.

I am the Lord your God. You shall not have strange gods before me.

You shall not take the name of the Lord your God in vain.

Honor your father and your mother.

You shall not kill.

Remember to keep holy the Lord's day.

You shall not covet your neighbor's goods.

You shall not steal.

You shall not bear false witness.

You shall not commit adultery.

You shall not covet your neighbor's wife.

CHAPTER 15

Confession

MEMORY VERSE: 1 John 1:9

"But if we confess our sins to God, He will keep His promise and do what is right: He will forgive us our sins and purify us from all our wrongdoing."

WHAT IS CONFESSION & WHY DO WE HAVE TO GO?

In previous chapters, we have discussed how we are all sinners that need to be saved. For that reason, Jesus came and died for us and for our salvation. But, it does not end there.

Jesus died in order for us to be able to go to heaven. However, we cannot get there with all of our sins attached to us.
  ☆This is as if someone has given you an invitation to the fanciest birthday party in the whole world. You can get in, you have an invitation. But you cannot get into the party without showering and brushing your hair and wearing your nicest clothes, right?

That is what confession is all about – it is like a spiritual shower. Through confession we are cleansing ourselves of our sins in order to be worthy of the presence of God.

In this chapter's Memory Verse, St. John is explaining that if we confess our sins, we will be able to live with God forever in heaven as He promised. BUT, we must confess in order for this to happen.

Did you know that Jesus Himself was the one who created confession? Open your Bible to John 20:21-23.
  ☆Who were the first priests? The 12 Disciples!
  ☆What is Jesus giving the 12 Disciples authority to do? Forgive sins.

Jesus Himself gave the priests the Sacrament of Confession. That is why we must go to a priest for confession. This is the way Jesus wants us to tell God our sins. He is there waiting for us in the confessional. Jesus and all the angels and saints rejoice so much when any one person goes to confession and is cleansed of their sins. Jesus is there through the priest waiting for you with open arms.

It is important to go to confession as often as possible. The Church suggests once a month. Like we said before, think of this as a spiritual shower. Would you take a bath only once a year? No, of course not! Just like we need to keep our bodies on the outside clean, we need to keep our souls on the inside clean by going to confession.

HOW DO WE MAKE A GOOD CONFESSION?

The most important thing for you to understand is that even though going to confession may seem hard (admitting that you did something wrong and apologizing is not always easy), it is a place of VICTORY.

There is great treasure and beauty found in the confessional. Jesus is right there waiting for you with open arms and He is so excited that you are turning away from your sins and coming back to Him. So even if it seems difficult and you are nervous, do not be afraid! Jesus, your greatest friend, is there waiting for you!

When you go to confession, there are 7 main things that are happening:

☆**Your Sins are Being Taken Away**

From this point on, the sins you confess are completely erased and you are cleansed of those sins.

☆**Increases Your Treasures in Heaven**

Every time you go to confession, you become sinless again, which gets you closer to God, which gets you closer to heaven.

☆**Helps Me Say No to Sin & Helps Me to be Good**

When we talk to the priest and he gives us advice and our penance, it helps us to be more aware of our sins and to hopefully do better in the future.

☆**Makes My Soul More Beautiful & Restores Grace to My Soul**

Remember how we talked about showering for the party? Well confession is that spiritual shower that makes your soul beautiful. Anything that is clean and nice is always more beautiful than dirty, right?

☆**Reconciles Me with Jesus**

Who is Jesus? Our friend! So confession is basically like coming to our best friend to apologize for all the ways we have hurt Him.

Remember, our sins are the reason He was nailed to the cross. Every time we sin or do something bad, we are putting Him on the cross again.

Confession is how we come back to Jesus and say sorry for causing Him that great pain.

Penance

What is penance? If we already confessed and apologized, what else is left to do?

Imagine there was a young boy who (whether on purpose or not) broke his neighbors window with his baseball. The young boy goes over to his neighbor's house and apologizes for breaking the window. The neighbor accepts the apology but tells the boy that he must mow his lawn for one month in order to repay him for the broken window.

Going to confession is our apology to God. But we need to make up for that sin somehow. So, the priest gives us penance. The penance is always different depending on the priest and the sins you committed.

It can be anything from saying a prayer, to reading a book in the Bible, or doing an act of charity for someone. The most important thing is that you do your penance as soon as possible to make sure your sins are wiped clean. The sins will not be wiped clean until your penance is complete.

The Act of Contrition

At the end of our confession we say this prayer in order to tell God we are sorry and that we truly mean it. We recognize our sins and that we have failed to obey God's commandments.

We tell God that we will do better and we ask Him for His help to do so. We state that Jesus is our Savior and only with His mercy can we be forgiven and saved. You can find the Act of Contrition prayer on page 97.

CONFESSION CHECKLIST

Pray to the Holy Spirit and ask Him to help you be honest and remember your sins. Look at your life through the Ten Commandments and make a checklist to help you make a good confession.

1. I am the Lord your God. You shall not have strange gods before me.

Have I made earthly things more important than God?　　Y＿＿＿　N＿＿＿

Have I made an idol of sports or entertainment figures?　　Y＿＿＿　N＿＿＿

2. You shall not take the name of the Lord your God in vain.

Have I used God's name carelessly?　　Y＿＿＿　N＿＿＿

Have I used God's name in anger?　　Y＿＿＿　N＿＿＿

Have I used bad language?　　Y＿＿＿　N＿＿＿

3. Remember to keep holy the Lord's day.

Did I attend Holy Mass every Sunday?　　Y＿＿＿　N＿＿＿

Did my behavior make it harder for my family to get to church on time?　Y＿＿＿　N＿＿＿

Have I remembered to pray daily?　　Y＿＿＿　N＿＿＿

4. Honor your father and your mother.

Have I obeyed and respected my parents?　　Y＿＿＿　N＿＿＿

Have I done my chores without complaining?　　Y＿＿＿　N＿＿＿

Have I been respectful to teachers, coaches, and others in authority?　Y＿＿＿　N＿＿＿

5. You shall not kill.

Have I been patient and kind with others?　　Y＿＿＿　N＿＿＿

Have I been unfair to others, especially those different than me?　　Y＿＿＿　N＿＿＿

Have I said mean things about other people?　　Y＿＿＿　N＿＿＿

TURN THE PAGE!

6. You shall not commit adultery.

Have I shown respect for my body?   Y_____ N_____

Have I respected the bodies of others?   Y_____ N_____

7. You shall not steal.

Have I taken something that belongs to someone else?   Y_____ N_____

Have I returned all the things that I have borrowed?   Y_____ N_____

8. You shall not bear false witness.

Have I played fairly and not cheated in school or games?   Y_____ N_____

Have I been honest and not lied?   Y_____ N_____

Have I hurt someone by what I have said or done?   Y_____ N_____

9. You shall not covet your neighbor's wife.

Have I been jealous of the friends that someone else has?   Y_____ N_____

10. You shall not covet your neighbor's goods.

Have I been jealous of the things that my friends have?   Y_____ N_____

Have I asked my parents to buy me things because my friends have them?   Y_____ N_____

STEPS TO MAKING A GOOD CONFESSION

Go through your Confession Checklist and write out your sins below. Because confession is private (between you and the priest), this paper is meant to be a guide for you to learn how to go to confession and to be able to remember your sins. Use this as practice for when you are in the confessional with the priest.

_____

_____

_____

_____

_____

_____

In the confessional with the priest, follow the below steps:

1. Make the Sign of the Cross.
2. Say, "Forgive me, Father, for I have sinned. This is my first confession."
3. Tell the priest the sins you have committed.
4. Once you finish, say, "Father, I am sorry for these sins and all the sins I may have forgotten."
5. Listen to the priest as he tells you how to be a better person.
6. Listen to the penance that the priest gives you.
7. Say the Act of Contrition:

> My God, I am sorry for my sins with all my heart.
> In choosing to do wrong and failing to do good,
> I have sinned against you
> Whom I should love above all things.
> I firmly intend, with Your help, to do penance, to sin no more,
> and to avoid whatever leads me to sin.
> Our Savior Jesus Christ suffered and died for us.
> In His name, my God, have mercy. Amen.

8. The priest says the words of absolution and blesses you.
9. Thank the priest and leave.
10. Do your penance as soon as possible.

The Seven Treasures of Confession
color each treasure!

Helps Me to be Good

My Sins Are Being Taken Away

Restores Grace to My Soul

Increases My Treasures in Heaven

Makes My Soul More Beautiful

Helps Me Say No to Sin

Reconciles Me With Jesus

CHAPTER 16

The Holy Eucharist

MEMORY VERSE: John 6:35

"'I am the bread of life,' Jesus told them. 'Those who come to me will never be hungry; those who believe in me will never be thirsty.'"

WHAT ARE WE RECEIVING?

In the above Memory Verse, what does Jesus mean when He says He is "the bread of life?"
☆We need to not only take His Body and Blood in Holy Communion but also <u>BELIEVE</u> that we are taking His real and actual Body and Blood. That is how we are fully saved.

TRANSUBSTANTIATION

Transubstantiation is the miraculous change of the bread and wine to the Body and Blood of Jesus Christ. You will hear that the Holy Eucharist is just a symbol. <u>THIS IS NOT TRUE.</u> The Holy Eucharist is the Sacrament that contains the Body and Blood (Soul and Divinity) of Jesus Christ. It is given to us under the appearances of bread and wine. So even though the Holy Eucharist looks and tastes like bread and wine, we know that it is truly the Body and Blood of Jesus. Jesus Christ gave priests the power to do this miracle and we believe it because Jesus is always faithful and true.

During Holy Mass, when the priest prays over the bread and wine (at the time of Consecration), what words is he saying?
☆Jesus' words at the Last Supper.

At this special time, what happens to the bread and wine?
☆They turn into the Body and Blood of Jesus.

When the priest is giving us Holy Communion in Church, what are we receiving?
☆The REAL Body and Blood of Jesus!

But what does it taste like?
☆Bread & Wine

How can something that looks like one thing, actually be another?

☆ ACTIVITY ☆

EGG ANALOGY

You will need a hardboiled egg, a raw egg, two bowls, and an adult for this activity.

Examine both eggs and mix up which is raw and which is hard boiled. Do they look the same? Are they the same?

Drop both eggs in separate bowls. They look and feel the same on the outside, but have completely different characteristics on the inside.

That is what transubstantiation is – the bread and wine look and feel the same on the outside but the words of Consecration (the words of Jesus) have changed them to be His Body and Blood.

WHY DO WE NEED THE HOLY EUCHARIST?
Open your Bible to the Memory Verse from chapter 7, Matthew 28:20b.

⭐Remember the parable of The Good Shepherd? Jesus is the Good Shepherd. He cares for us, loves us, and is ALWAYS with us. What is the best way to keep Jesus close to us and keep Him with us always? Through the Holy Eucharist. When we receive the Holy Eucharist, it is called Holy Communion.

What does Holy Communion do?
⭐Makes us Holy.
⭐Unites us as close as possible to Jesus Christ.
⭐Gives us power to keep away from evil.
⭐Prepares us for eternal life in heaven.
⭐Helps us remember what Jesus did for us on the cross.

Open your Bible to John 6:56.
⭐Jesus ALWAYS wants us to be close to Him – and the closer we are to Him, the further we are from the devil and evil. So, what is the best way to stay close to Him and have Him alive in us? HOLY COMMUNION.

———————————— ⭐ ACTIVITY ⭐ ————————————

CUP ANALOGY

You will need an empty cup, a pitcher of water, and an adult for this activity.

Examine your empty glass – there is so much room to fill it up with anything – good, nice things, bad ideas, evil, etc...

Imagine the pitcher of water is all good things from God. Fill the glass up with water to the very top (all the way to the brim!). If you make sure to only fill yourself up with Jesus in Holy Communion, prayer, and good works, then there is absolutely no room for anything else to enter. But, we have to make sure we empty our glass from all evil (for example, jealousy, anger, lying, disobedience) in order to only leave room for Our Lord.

And that is what Jesus is asking us to do. We should follow His commandments and partake in Holy Communion so we can always be close to Him here on earth and, one day, in heaven.

————————————————

RESPECT FOR HOLY COMMUNION
Because that is Jesus up at the altar whom we will receive, how should we act in His presence? If the pope were to walk through the door right now, how would you act? Would you maybe sit up straight? Would you be respectful? Polite? If you would do all these things for the pope, who is just a human being that represents Jesus on earth, would you not do SO MUCH more for our Lord and Savior who is the King of heaven and earth?

That is our King up at the altar. The only friend that we have who died on the cross for us. He deserves all of our love and respect. Remember the chapter about the Holy Mass and the respect we should have in Church? Kneeling and bowing in front of the tabernacle? That is why we do these things. Because He is present.

Also, it is very important to be in friendship with God before receiving Holy Communion. So if you think you have committed any serious sins, you must go to Confession before you receive Holy Communion. It is important that our hearts and minds are pure and clean when we receive Jesus Christ into our bodies.

WHAT IS EUCHARISTIC ADORATION?
There is one more very important way to grow closer to Jesus – going to EUCHARISTIC ADORATION.

Eucharistic Adoration is time we spend praying to Jesus in the Church when the Holy Eucharist is exposed.

The priest places the exposed Holy Eucharist in a monstrance in the Church for us to quietly spend time in prayer with Jesus who is fully present: Body, Blood, Soul, and Divinity. By doing this, we are actively deepening our relationship with Him.

What is a monstrance?
☆ A monstrance is a decorated article, usually made of gold or silver, that displays the Holy Eucharist.

MONSTRANCE

Why do we do this?
☆ FIRST: The Influence. If I have friends that are really good, loving, and spread joy, I will most likely do the same. Who is the greatest, most loving, most joyous, wonderful friend ever? JESUS. So, if I spend as much time as possible with Jesus one on one in Adoration, don't you think I might end up acting and being more like Jesus? YES!

☆ SECOND: To Spend Time With Your Friend. This is how you can grow closer to Jesus, by spending time with Him. Be there. Offer Him all your love and watch your relationship grow stronger.

☆ THIRD: Talking to Jesus & Jesus Talking to You. Prayer is how you talk to God, right? Well, in Eucharistic Adoration, you give God another way to talk to you. You offer up your intentions, hopes, dreams, worries, sadness, love, thanksgiving, and all of your feelings during this time. You have a conversation with your best friend who will answer you as He always does.

Open your Bible to 1 Peter 5:7.
☆ Jesus wants us to give Him all our troubles because He cares for us and will always help us.

Jesus' help comes at different times and in all different shapes and sizes. Sometimes we get a clear answer and that help is immediate, and sometimes it takes much longer. But know that Jesus is ALWAYS looking out for your best interest and everything happens for a reason in His perfect plan for you.

YOU ARE SO VERY LOVED!

The Holy Eucharist

1. Read John 6:35. What does Jesus mean when He says that He is the "Bread of Life?"

_____

_____

_____

2. During the part of the mass when the priest reads Jesus' words at the Last Supper (Consecration), what is happening?

_____

_____

3. What is Transubstantiation?

_____

_____

_____

TURN THE PAGE!

4. Why is receiving the REAL Body and Blood of Jesus so important for us in our lives?

_____

_____

_____

_____

_____

5. How can we make sure that we stay close to Jesus?

_____

_____

_____

_____

_____

6. Because Jesus is up at the altar at the moment of Consecration, how should we act in His presence during mass?

_____

_____

_____

7. What is Eucharistic Adoration?

_____

_____

_____

Holy Eucharist & the REAL Presence of Jesus
☆ ACTIVITY ☆

INSTRUCTIONS:

1. Color the heading, host, and chalice.

2. Cut the heading and chalice out. Cut the host along the dotted line but make sure to leave the middle where the circles meet uncut (you will fold along this line once it is cut out).

3. Cut out the below image of Jesus. Glue the image of Jesus on the inside of the folded host (on the opposite side of "Glue this side to construction paper").

4. On a piece of construction paper, glue the heading to the top of the paper.

5. Glue the host to the construction paper towards the top, under the heading. Glue the chalice underneath the host.

WHAT YOU'LL NEED:
- ☆ Scissors
- ☆ Crayons
- ☆ Glue Stick
- ☆ Colorful Construction Paper

IMAGE OF JESUS

HEADING - cut out

HOLY EUCHARIST
The Real Body and Blood of Jesus

FOLD LINE -
do not cut through,
only cut around!

Glue this side
to construction paper

†

"I am the bread of life"
John 6:35a

HOST

CHALICE - cut out

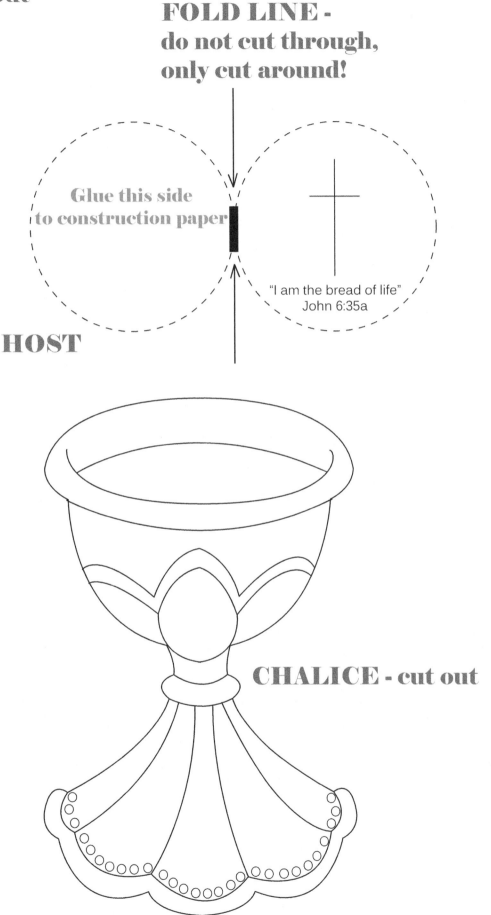

Prayers to Keep Close to Your Heart

THE ROSARY & WHY WE PRAY IT
The Rosary is a series of prayers that follows a string of Rosary beads: 1 Our Father, 10 Hail Marys, 1 Doxology, 1 Fatima Prayer – repeated 5 times.

The Rosary guides us through the life of Jesus and helps us learn from it. The different parts (or events) of Jesus' life are called "The Mysteries." The Mysteries of the Rosary guide us through the lives of Jesus and Mary and what these events can teach us in our everyday lives.

Depending on the day, we follow the life of Jesus through the Mysteries. Each Mystery has a "Fruit" we can learn from. For example, the second Mystery of the Joyful Mysteries is "The Visitation." This is when Mary was pregnant with Jesus and went to help her cousin Elizabeth who was pregnant with John the Baptist. Putting another's needs before her own, Mary traveled very far just to be with Elizabeth. The Fruit of this Mystery is "Love of Neighbor" – teaching us to love one another selflessly.

HOW DO WE PRAY THE ROSARY?

1. Make the Sign of the Cross
2. Pray the Apostle's Creed (slightly different from the Nicene Creed)
3. Pray the Our Father (shown in BLUE beads)
4. Pray 3 Hail Marys (shown in GREEN beads) and 1 Doxology
5. Announce the mystery and pray the Our Father
6. Pray 10 Hail Marys and 1 Doxology
7. Pray the Fatima Prayer

<u>Repeat steps 5-7 until you have completed the Circle and then pray the Concluding Prayers.</u>

APOSTLE'S CREED
I believe in God, the Father Almighty, Creator of heaven and earth; and in Jesus Christ, His only Son, our Lord; Who was conceived by the Holy Spirit, born of the Virgin Mary, suffered under Pontius Pilate, was crucified, died, and was buried.
He descended into hell; the third day He arose again from the dead. He ascended into heaven, and sits at the right hand of God, the Father Almighty; from thence He shall come to judge the living and the dead. I believe in the Holy Spirit, the Holy Catholic Church, the communion of Saints, the forgiveness of sins, the resurrection of the body and life everlasting. Amen.

FATIMA PRAYER
Oh my Jesus, forgive us our sins. Save us from the fires of hell. Lead all souls to Heaven, especially those in most need of Thy mercy.

THE MYSTERIES OF THE ROSARY FOR EACH DAY

The Joyful Mysteries
(said on Mondays & Saturdays)

The Annunciation – when Gabriel visited Mary, announcing the birth of Jesus
  Fruit of the Mystery: Humility
The Visitation – when Mary visited Elizabeth while pregnant
  Fruit of the Mystery: Love of neighbor
The Nativity – when Jesus was born in a manger in Bethlehem
  Fruit of the Mystery: Poverty of spirit
The Presentation – when Mary and Joseph took Jesus to the temple as a baby
  Fruit of the Mystery: Obedience
The Finding in the Temple – when Mary and Joseph found Jesus after three days
  Fruit of the Mystery: Piety

The Sorrowful Mysteries
(said on Tuesdays & Fridays)

The Agony in the Garden – when Jesus prayed in the Garden before being captured
  Fruit of the Mystery: Conformity to the Will of God
The Scourging at the Pillar – when Jesus was tortured
  Fruit of the Mystery: Purity and mortification

The Crowning of the Thorns – when the guards mocked Jesus with a crown of thorns
  Fruit of the Mystery: Moral courage
The Carrying of the Cross
  Fruit of the Mystery: Patience

The Crucifixion of Our Lord – when Jesus died on the cross
  Fruit of the Mystery: Salvation

Glorious Mysteries
(said on Wednesdays & Sundays)

The Resurrection – when Jesus rose from the dead
  Fruit of the Mystery: Faith

The Ascension – when Jesus went up to heaven
  Fruit of the Mystery: Hope, desire for heaven

The Descent of the Holy Spirit – when the Holy Spirit came down on Pentecost
  Fruit of the Mystery: Wisdom and Love of God
The Assumption – When Jesus took His mother to heaven
  Fruit of the Mystery: Devotion to Mary
The Coronation of Our Lady – Mary being crowned Queen of heaven and earth
  Fruit of the Mystery: Eternal happiness

Luminous Mysteries
(said on Thursdays)

The Baptism in the Jordan – when John the Baptist baptized Jesus
  Fruit of the Mystery: Openness to the Holy Spirit
The Wedding at Cana – where Jesus performed His first miracle
  Fruit of the Mystery: To Jesus through Mary
The Proclamation of the Kingdom of Heaven – Jesus announced the coming of the Kingdom of Heaven through His teachings
  Fruit of the Mystery: Repentance, Trust in God
The Transfiguration of Our Lord – when Jesus went up to the mountain and Elijah and Moses appeared
  Fruit of the Mystery: Desire for holiness
The Institution of the Eucharist – the Last Supper, where we are given Holy Communion
  Fruit of the Mystery: Eucharistic Adoration

CONCLUDING PRAYERS

Hail Holy Queen, Mother of Mercy, our life, our sweetness, and our hope. To thee do we cry, poor banished children of Eve. To thee do we send up our sighs, mourning, and weeping in this valley of tears. Turn then, most gracious advocate, thine eyes of mercy towards us, and after this, our exile, show unto us the Blessed Fruit of thy womb, Jesus. O Clement, O Loving, O Sweet Virgin Mary. Pray for us, O Holy Mother of God, that we may be made worthy of the promises of Christ. Amen.

O God, whose only-begotten Son, by His life, death, and resurrection, has purchased for us the rewards of eternal life, grant, we beseech Thee, that meditating upon these mysteries of the Most Holy Rosary of the Blessed Virgin Mary, we may imitate what they contain and obtain what they promise, through the same Christ our Lord. Amen.

Prayers to Keep Close to Your Heart

ST. PATRICK'S MORNING PRAYER

As I arise today, may the strength of God pilot me, the power of God uphold me, the wisdom of God guide me.
May the eye of God look before me, the ear of God hear me, the word of God speak for me.
May the hand of God protect me, the way of God lie before me, the shield of God defend me, the host of God save me.
May Christ shield me today... Christ with me, Christ before me, Christ behind me, Christ in me, Christ beneath me, Christ above me, Christ on my right, Christ on my left, Christ when I lie down, Christ when I sit, Christ when I stand, Christ in the heart of everyone who thinks of me, Christ in the mouth of everyone who speaks of me, Christ in every eye that sees me, Christ in every ear that hears me.

BEDTIME PRAYER

Heavenly Father,
Thank you for the day you gave to us.
Please bless (insert name) and keep him/her in your love and protection.
Grant him/her a good night's sleep tonight and send your guardian angels to watch over him/her while he/she sleeps.
In the name of the Father, and the Son, and the Holy Spirit. Amen.

GRACE BEFORE MEALS

Bless us, O Lord, and these Thy gifts, which we are about to receive from Thy bounty, through Christ our Lord. Amen.

SERENITY PRAYER

God, grant me the serenity
to accept the things I cannot change
the courage to change the things I can
and the wisdom to know the difference.

ST. PADRE PIO'S AFTER COMMUNION PRAYER

Stay with me, Lord, for it is necessary to have You present so that I do not forget You. You know how easily I abandon You.
Stay with me, Lord, because I am weak and I need Your strength, that I may not fall so often.
Stay with me, Lord, for You are my life, and without You, I am without fervor.
Stay with me, Lord, for You are my light, and without You, I am in darkness.
Stay with me, Lord, to show me Your will.
Stay with me, Lord, so that I hear Your voice and follow You.
Stay with me, Lord, for I desire to love You very much, and always be in Your company.
With a firm love, I will love You with all my heart while on earth
and continue to love You perfectly during all eternity. Amen.

MEMORARE

Remember, O most gracious Virgin Mary, that never was it known that anyone who fled to thy protection, implored thy help, or sought thine intercession was left unaided.

Inspired by this confidence, I fly unto thee, O Virgin of virgins, my mother; to thee do I come, before thee I stand, sinful and sorrowful. O Mother of the Word Incarnate, despise not my petitions, but in thy mercy hear and answer me. Amen.

ST. MICHAEL THE ARCHANGEL

Saint Michael the Archangel, defend us in battle. Be our protection against the wickedness and snares of the devil; May God rebuke him, we humbly pray; And do thou, O Prince of the Heavenly Host, by the power of God, thrust into hell Satan and all the evil spirits who prowl about the world seeking the ruin of souls. Amen.

CHAPTER 1: GOD'S LOVE THROUGH THE BIBLE

THE PRODIGAL SON

4 The father runs to welcome his younger son, hugs and kisses him

3 The younger son comes to realize that he has sinned and decides to return to his father's house

5 The older son gets upset that his younger brother is welcomed back with a feast and celebration

2 The younger son starves and is left with nothing

6 The father explains that both sons are loved so much and are always welcome in his home

1 The younger son took his share of the property/money and left his father's home

MEANING OF THE PARABLE:
Our Father loves and welcomes all his children

THE THREE SERVANTS

4 The servant who had 1,000 coins dug a hole in the ground and hid the money

6 The master punishes the servant who buried the money and throws him into the darkness

1 The master leaves his servants in charge of his property, splitting it according to their abilities

2 The servant who had 5,000 coins invested it and doubled the money

5 The servants who doubled their money and used it wisely were greatly rewarded when their master returned

3 The servant who had 2,000 coins invested it and doubled the money

MEANING OF THE PARABLE:
We should always use the talents God gives us

CHAPTER 2: GUARDIAN ANGELS, SAINTS, & 3 T'S

1. What are the 3 T's? Time, Talent, and Treasure

2. How can you give your TIME to God? Some examples include (but are not limited to) prayer, reading the Bible, and helping others.

3. How can you give your TALENTS to God? Some examples include (but are not limited to) Singing in Church, visiting the sick and elderly, teaching, praying for each others, feeding the hungry, consoling the lonely, being kind.

4. How can you give your TREASURE to God? Giving money to Church and giving money to the poor.

CHAPTER 4: THE TRINITY

1. Who are the 3 Persons of the Trinity? God the Father, God the Son, and God the Holy Spirit

2. Each Person of the Trinity helps us in different ways. Through the Bible, what role did we find for each Person?

God the Father - Matthew 6:25-34: My Father

God the Son - John 15:7-17: My Friend

God the Holy Spirit - Galatians 5:22-26: My Teacher

3. According to Galatians 5:22-23, what are the nine fruits of the Holy Spirit? Love, Kindness, Peace, Joy, Patience, Humility, Goodness, Faithfulness, and Self-Control

CHAPTER 5: THE VIRGIN MARY

1. Mary appears in the Gospel 7 times. List those 7 times: The Annunciation, the Visitation, the Nativity, the Presentation of Jesus, the Finding of Jesus in the Temple, the Wedding at Cana, and at the Foot of the Cross.

2. When the angel Gabriel came to Mary and explained to her that she will have a Son and that He will be the Savior of the world, what was her answer? Yes.

3. When and where does Jesus give us Mary as our Mother? At the foot of the cross before He dies.

4. If we look to Mary our Mother and ask for her guidance, who will she always lead us to? Her Son, Jesus.

CHAPTER 6: GOD'S FIELD

1. We grow on the outside (physically) by eating, sleeping, and exercising. How do we grow on the inside in our relationship with God (spiritually)? Some examples include (but are not limited to) praying, going to Church every Sunday, following God's Commandments, and reading the Bible.

2. What is Jesus telling us through the Parable of the Sower? We should be the good soil for God's Word to be fruitful in our hearts.

3. What does each part of the parable stand for?

The Sower (Man Planting the Seeds): God

The Seeds: The Word of God

The Path: those who hear God's words but the devil takes the message away, making them not have faith.

The Rocks: those who hear God's words and are filled with joy. But they have no roots so when hard times come, their faith dies.

The Thorn Bushes: those who hear God's words but are so worried with riches and pleasures in life that their faith dies.

The Rich Soil: those who hear God's Word, have true faith, and continue to believe no matter what. They grow closer to God and bear good fruit.

CHAPTER 7: THE GOOD SHEPHERD

1. What does each part of the parable stand for?

The Shepherd: Jesus   The Wolf: The devil

The Sheep: Us, God's children   The Hired Man: People that pretend to be our shepherd but they do not really love or care for us.

2. What does a Good Shepherd do? How is Jesus the Good Shepherd? A good shepherd lays down His life for His sheep. Jesus is the Good Shepherd because He did lay down His life for us.

3. Jesus came so that we can have life in its fullness. How can we have that through Him? Jesus came to save us and if we follow God's commands just as Jesus did, we will have eternal life with Him.

CHAPTER 8: THE CHURCH, ONE BODY

1. Who is the Head of the Church? Jesus

2. Just like our physical bodies have many different parts, the Body of Christ also has many different parts. Who are the different parts? We are the different parts of the Church Body

3. Read 1 Corinthians 12:12-26. What is the St. Paul saying about the different parts of the Body of Christ? That all parts of the Church Body are important and needed for the Body to be healthy.

CHAPTER 9: CHURCH ORGANIZATION

1. Who created the Church structure and appointed the first Pope? Jesus

2. Who was the first pope? St. Peter

3. Who is the current pope? - - - - - - - - - - - - -

4. As part of the "Laity" in the Church, what are ways you can get involved to keep the Body of Christ alive? Each child will have a different answer based on their talents and interests.

CHAPTER 10: THE HOLY MASS

1. What is the best way to strengthen our relationship with God? By going to Church not only every Sunday but as often as we can.

2. Why do we fast one hour before receiving Holy Communion? To prepare ourselves for the REAL presence of Jesus into our body and soul. Fasting also separates us from worldly things which brings us closer to God.

3. According to the dress code chart, circle yes or no if the items of clothing listed below are appropriate for Church:

   Shorts: NO   Polo Shirts: YES   Pants: YES   Slippers: NO

4. Why should we arrive to Church before Holy Mass starts? So we can prepare ourselves for mass. We kneel before Jesus to thank Him, praise Him, and offer Him our intentions.

5. What are we celebrating during Holy Mass? The Life, Death, and Resurrection of Jesus

6. What happens during Consecration? The priest reads the words of Jesus from the Last Supper and the bread and wine change into the REAL Body and Blood of Jesus.

7. Why is it important to offer our intentions to God? Because God always wants us to bring Him our intentions and to come to Him for whatever we need.

8. What did St. Augustine mean when he said "Become what you receive" as he gave Holy Communion? Once you receive the Body and Blood of Jesus, you should do your best to be just like the Lord Jesus - loving, kind, and forgiving.

CHAPTER 10: THE HOLY MASS CROSSWORD PUZZLE

DOWN

1. Dressed
2. Baptism
3. Bow
4. Angel
5. Homily
6. Creed
7. Treasure
8. Blood
9. Receive
10. Final

ACROSS

1. Mass
2. Fast
3. Body
4. Intentions
5. Last Supper
6. Celebration

CHAPTER 11: FAITH, HOPE, & LOVE

1. Out of Faith, Hope, & Love, which does St. Paul say is the greatest? LOVE

2. How many times is "Do Not be Afraid" in the Bible? 365 times

3. What do we learn about Faith from the story about Peter walking on the water? That with faith anything is possible. When Peter had faith, he walked on water. When he was afraid, he began to sink. Fear is the opposite of faith.

4. Fear is good for our faith. FALSE

5. Having hope increases our faith. TRUE

6. What does it mean to have Hope in the Resurrection? Jesus has given us hope in His Resurrection, that we will one day be in heaven with Him and all the ones that we love that have died before us.

7. In John 13:34, what is Jesus commanding us to do? "Love one another as I have loved you."

8. How can we show our love for each other? By being kind, helpful, compassionate, a good friend, etc. (Give your own examples). When we show love for one another, we are showing Jesus how much we love Him as well.

CHAPTER 12: DISCIPLESHIP

1. Who were the original 12 Disciples of Jesus? (Simon) Peter, John, Simon, Philip, Thomas, Andrew, Bartholomew, James, Matthew, James, the Less, Jude, and Judas.

2. In Luke 5:10, what did Jesus say to Peter? "Don't be afraid, from now on you will be catching people."

3. What does Jesus mean when he says "you will be catching people?" From now on they will no longer catching fish, they will be catching people – they will be bringing people to Jesus as His disciples.

4. How can we be active disciples of Jesus? By keeping our light for Jesus shining bright. By being kind and spreading love we are doing Jesus' work. We never know how our example can be saving someone and bringing them to Jesus.

CHAPTER 13: THE TEN COMMANDMENTS

1. Which book of the Bible can the Ten Commandments be found? Exodus

2. Who were the original Ten Commandments given to? Moses

3. How can we obey the 1st Commandment? By keeping God first in our lives, NO MATTER WHAT.

4. Which day of the week is the "Lord's day"? Sunday

5. The 5th Commandment is ONLY about physically killing someone. FALSE

6. What does the 8th Commandment mean? We should never lie - always be honest.

7. What are the 9th and 10th commandments about? Jealousy

8. In James 3:14-15, what is St. James saying about jealousy? What is the best way to guard your heart from jealousy? Jealousy is ugly and from this world (demonic). It is not an emotion that comes from God and we have to be very careful to guard our hearts from it. The best way to do this is to always be thankful for what you have. Being grateful for what God has blessed us with and only focus on that – not what others around us have.

CHAPTER 15: THE SEVEN SACRAMENTS

1. A sacrament is a Visible sign of an Invisible Grace that is given by God.

2. What are the 7 Sacraments? Baptism, Confirmation, Confession, Holy Communion, Matrimony, Holy Order, & Anointing of the Sick

3. Why did Jesus come into the world? Jesus came into the world to save us so we can have eternal life with Him.

4. Each Sacrament has a grace and a sign. List the grace and sign for the Sacrament of Baptism:
     Grace: Makes you a child of God
     Sign: Washing with Holy Water in the name of the Father, and the Son, and the Holy Spirit

5. Each Sacrament has a grace and a sign. List the grace and sign for the Sacrament of Matrimony:
     Grace: Makes holy the love between a man and a woman
     Sign: Blessing and Crowns

6. What does the Memory Verse, Ephesians 2:8-9, say about grace and faith? We have been saved by grace through faith – even when we did not deserve it God still loves us, protects us, forgives us, and has sent us His only Son as a Savior for us. If we believe in Him, we are saved.

CHAPTER 16: THE HOLY EUCHARIST

1. Read John 6:35. What does Jesus mean when He says that He is the "Bread of Life?" We need to not only take His Body and Blood in Communion but also BELIEVE that we are taking His real and actual Body and Blood. That is how we are closest to Jesus and will be saved.

2. During the part of the mass when the priest reads Jesus' words at the Last Supper (the Consecration), what is happening? The bread and wine are being changed into the Body and Blood of Jesus.

3. What is Transubstantiation? Transubstantiation is the miraculous change of the bread and wine to Body and Blood. At consecration, they become the Body and Blood of Christ while keeping only the appearances of bread and wine.

4. Why is receiving the REAL Body and Blood of Jesus so important for us in our lives? The more we receive the REAL Body and Blood of Jesus, the closer we will be to Him. The closer we are to Jesus, the further we are from the devil and evil. This will help us here on earth and help get us to heaven.

5. How can we make sure that we stay close Jesus? (Answers will vary) Follow His commandments, do good works, and take Communion as often as possible.

6. Because Jesus is up at the altar at the moment of Consecration, how should we act in His presence during mass? We should be respectful, quiet, loving, and grateful while we praise Him.

7. What is Eucharistic Adoration? When a priest places the exposed Eucharist in the Church for us to quietly spend time in prayer with Jesus who is present – Body, Blood, Soul, and Divinity. In this time we show our love and respect for Jesus by being with Him.

NOTES

NOTES

NOTES

NOTES

NOTES

NOTES

The Beginning.

Made in the USA
Coppell, TX
11 October 2021